Nancy Roser

Professor, Language and Literacy Studies
Department of Curriculum and Instruction
The University of Texas at Austin

Macmillan/McGraw–Hill

Columbus, Ohio

Credits

Illustrations: Steve McInturff
Electronic Illustrations: Jennie Copeland, Tom Goodwin
Heads: John Kurtz
Cover: Bob Ostrom

Printed in the United States of America

0-02-686182-8

 2 3 4 5 6 7 8 9 10 POH 01 00 99 98 97 96 95 94

How to Study a Word

① Look at the word.

What does it mean?
How is it spelled?

print

② Say the word.

What sounds do you hear?
Are there any silent letters?

print

③ Think about the word.

How is each sound spelled?
Do you see any word parts?

pr i nt

④ Write the word.

Did you copy all the letters carefully?
Did you think about the sounds
and letters?

print

⑤ Check the spelling.

Did you spell the word correctly?
Do you need to write it again?

print

Contents

Lesson   **Page**

1 Spelling the Short *a* Sound 2

2 Spelling the Short *i* Sound 6

3 Spelling the /o/ and /ô/ Sounds 10

4 Spelling the Final /k/ Sound 14

5 Spelling the /nd/ and /st/ Sounds 18

6 Review 22

7 Spelling the Short *e* Sound 24

8 Spelling the Short *u* Sound 28

9 Spelling Words with *dr, tr,* and *gr* 32

10 Spelling Words with *gl, bl,* and *pl* 36

11 Spelling Words That End with *sk, mp,* and *ng* 40

12 Review 44

13 Spelling the Long *a* Sound 46

14 Spelling the Long *e* Sound 50

15 Spelling the Long *i* Sound 54

16 Spelling the Long *o* Sound 58

17 Spelling the /ü/ Sound 62

18 Review 66

19 Spelling Words with *wh* and *sh* 68

20 Spelling Words with *ch* and *th* 72

21 Spelling the Vowel + *r* Sound 76

22 Spelling More Vowel + *r* Sounds 80

23 Easily Misspelled Words 84

24 Review 88

25 Spelling Words with *br, fr,* and *tr* 90

26 Spelling Words with *sl* and *sp* 94

27 Spelling Words Ending with *-s* 98

28 Spelling Words That Sound Alike 102

29 Spelling Family Names 106

30 Review 110

31 Spelling the /u̇/ Sound 112

32 Spelling Words Ending in *-ed* and *-ing* 116

33 Spelling the /ou/ Sound 120

34 Spelling Compound Words 124

35 Spelling Number Words 128

36 Review 132

Steps in the Writing Process 134

How To Use the Dictionary 136

Speller Dictionary 138

1

Spelling the Short *a* Sound

FOCUS

Sound	Sign	Spelling
short *a*	/a/	man hat

Say each word. Listen for the short *a* sound in *man* and *hat*.

Study the spelling. How is the short *a* vowel spelled?

Write the words.

1–10. Write the ten Core Words. Ring the letter that spells the short vowel sound.

11–15. Write the five Challenge Words. Ring the letter that spells the short vowel sound.

SPELLING TIP
The short *a* sound is often spelled *a*.

CORE

1. lap
2. man
3. hat
4. map
5. has
6. pat
7. mad
8. gas
9. fat
10. bad

CHALLENGE

11. as
12. jam
13. dash
14. path
15. cash

WORDS and MEANINGS

Complete the story with Core Words.

WHAT A DAY!

One day I went to the park to play. I like it there because it (1) swings and a slide. I saw a (2) sitting on a bench near the swings. He had a tall red (3) on his head. He was looking at a road (4). A white cat was sitting in his (5). It was big and (6). I wanted to (7) the fat cat.

The man looked (8). It was a very (9) day for him. The man could not find his way home and his car was out of (10). He had to walk all the way with his fat cat and his red hat!

Word Families

Change the first letter in each word to spell a Core Word. Write the words.

11. bat   13. nap   15. lad

12. can   14. cat

Fit the Letters Write the two Core Words that fit each puzzle.

1–2.

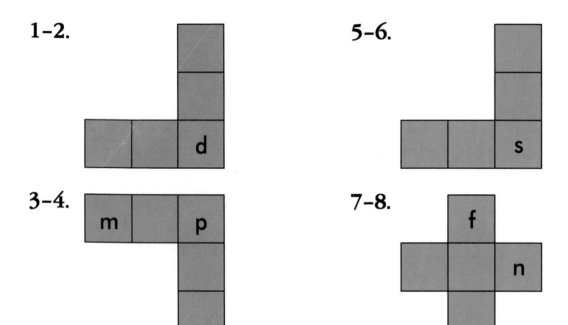

d

5–6.

s

3–4.

m   p

7–8.

f

n

Unscramble and Spell Write the Core Word by changing the order of the following letters.

9. ash

10. pal

11. tap

12. nam

Pair Up the Words Write the missing Core Word that goes with each word.

woman and ___   14. coat and ___   15. oil and ___

Write a story telling about a bad day that you had. Follow the steps on pages 134–135 to help you. Use three Core Words from this lesson.

Proofreding prakticee

1–3. Here is a story about a bad day. Three words are not spelled correctly. Write them correctly.

> Monday was a bed day. I spilled milk on my lup. After that I sat on my new hat. Then I could not find the state I live in on the mep. I was sad that day.

Now proofread your story and correct any mistakes.

CORE		CHALLENGE
lap	pat	as
man	mad	jam
hat	gas	dash
map	fat	path
has	bad	cash

Spelling the Short *i* Sound

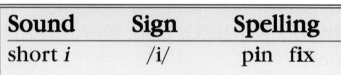

CORE

1. if
2. fix
3. pin
4. his
5. mix
6. rip
7. kiss
8. hid
9. tip
10. milk

CHALLENGE

11. dish
12. mitt
13. fish
14. rich
15. wish

Sound	Sign	Spelling
short *i*	/i/	pin fix

Say each word. Listen for the short *i* sound in *pin* and *fix*.

Study the spelling. How is the short vowel spelled?

Write the words.

1–10. Write the ten Core Words. Ring the letter that spells the short vowel sound.

11–15. Write the five Challenge Words. Ring the letter that spells the short vowel sound.

SPELLING TIP
The short *i* sound is often spelled *i*.

WORDS and MEANINGS

Complete the story with Core Words.

A Real Treat

Josh loves (1) mom. He wanted to do something that would make her happy. So he went into the kitchen to (2) her lunch.

Josh had to do many things to get ready. He had to (3) off the leaves from a head of lettuce. Next, he cut off the (4) of a carrot. Then he had to (5) the cooked vegetables. Finally, he poured her a glass of (6).

When Josh was finished, he tried to (7) a flower on his mom's napkin. Then he (8) a note under her dish. His mom gave him a big (9). Could you make lunch (10) you tried?

Opposites

Write the opposite of each word. Each answer will have a short *i* sound.

11. her   13. break   15. out
12. small   14. stand

Look and Write Write the Core Words that fit each clue.

1–2. Two Core Words that end with the letter *x*.

3–4. Two Core Words that end with two consonants.

5. The Core Word that has the word *in* in it.

6–7. Two Core Words that rhyme with *lip*.

Swap a Vowel Change the vowel in each word to make the Core Word. Write the word.

8.	tap ⇨
9.	has ⇨
10.	of ⇨
11.	had ⇨
12.	fox ⇨

Use the Dictionary Words in a dictionary are arranged in ABC order. Look at the first letter in each word. Write the word in each group that would come first in ABC order.

13. rip   pin   mix   15. rip   milk   kiss

14. hid   tip   if   16. milk   if   pin

You read about how a boy made his mom happy. Make a list of things you can do for someone you like. Use three Core Words from this lesson.

Prooofreding prakticee

a **c**

1–3. Here is a student's list. Three words are not spelled correctly. Write each word correctly.

1. Fex a broken toy ef I can.
2. Play a game.
3. Give a hug and a kis.

Now proofread your list and correct any mistakes.

CORE		CHALLENGE
if	rip	dish
fix	kiss	mitt
pin	hid	fish
his	tip	rich
mix	milk	wish

3 Spelling the /o/ and /ô/ Sounds

FOCUS

CORE

1. log
2. got
3. dog
4. job
5. lot
6. fog
7. flop
8. spot
9. jog
10. off

CHALLENGE

11. robin
12. soggy
13. slot
14. cross
15. cot

Sound	Sign	Spelling
short o	/o/	job
	/ô/	log

Say each word. Listen for the vowel sounds in *job* and *log*. Note the sign for each sound.

Study the spelling. How are these sounds spelled?

Write the words.

1–10. Write the ten Core Words. Ring the letter that spells the vowel sound.

11–15. Write the five Challenge Words. Ring the letter that spells the vowel sound.

SPELLING TIP

The short *o* and /ô/ sounds are often spelled *o*.

WORDS and MEANINGS

Complete the story with Core Words.

A GREAT JOB

Meg has a new (1) after school. She (2) the job last week. Meg is happy because she will now be able to save some cash. She wants to buy some new pet fish.

Meg's job is a (3) of fun. She takes a big black and white (4) for walks. She has to take the dog out every day in sun, rain, or (5).

Sometimes Meg takes the dog to a safe (6) and runs around with it. Other times she sits by herself on a (7) while the dog runs (8) by itself. Maybe one day she will (9) with the dog. Then they both will (10) down under a tree to rest.

More Than One

Add -s to each word to show more than one.

dog   dogs

11. one log, two ___

12. one spot, two___

13. one pot, two ___

14. one hog, two ___

15. one frog, two ___

16. one tot, two ___

Listen and Write
Write the Core Word that has the same ending sound as the picture words. Ring the Core Word that ends with two consonants.

1.

2.

3.

Rhyme and Answer
Write the missing Core Word. It will rhyme with the underlined word.

4. A place for a bed is a <u>cot</u> ____.

5. A wooden toy for a pet is a <u>dog</u> ____.

6. A yard for children is a <u>tot</u> ____.

Add Another Word
Think how the words in each group are alike. Write the Core Word that belongs in each group.

7. snow, sleet, rain, ____

8. fish, cat, bird, ____

9. walk, skip, run, ____

10. hot, spot, lot, ____

Follow the steps on pages 134–135 to write a letter to a friend about a job you would like. Use three Core Words from this lesson.

Prooofreding prakticee
(a) *(c)*

1–3. Here is a student's letter. Three words are not spelled correctly. Write each word correctly.

> Dear Rose,
>
> I got a jeb It is a lat of work. I wash our dog. I get off every spat of dirt My family likes my work. So does my dog.
>
> Your friend,
>
> Dan

4–5. Two periods are missing. Copy the letter and correct all mistakes.

CORE		CHALLENGE
log	fog	robin
got	flop	soggy
dog	spot	slot
job	jog	cross
lot	off	cot

4 Spelling the Final /k/ Sound

FOCUS

CORE

1. rock
2. kick
3. sack
4. dock
5. pack
6. sick
7. stack
8. lock
9. stick
10. snack

CHALLENGE

11. click
12. flock
13. shack
14. clock
15. backpack

Sound	Spelling
/k/	lo**ck**

Say each word. Listen for the last sound you hear in *lock*.

Study the spelling. How is this sound spelled?

Write the words.

1–10. Write the ten Core Words. Ring the letters that spell the last sound.

11–15. Write the five Challenge Words. Ring the letters that spell the last sound.

SPELLING TIP
A final /k/ sound is spelled *ck*.

WORDS and MEANINGS

Complete the story with Core Words.

A Busy Afternoon

Today I will go down to the boat (1) with my friend. There is a lot of trash on the dock. People should put their trash in the garbage. All the cans left around make me (2)! We will (3) them in a pile and take them to the dump.

Later we can (4) a ball around the yard. Then we can climb to the top of the big (5). We will (6) on apples and nuts. My friend and I will (7) the food in a bag. I will carry the paper (8) in my backpack. I will bring a long (9) to help me walk. I hope I will not forget to (10) my house door before I go.

Word Meaning

Write the Core Word that means the same or almost the same as each word.

11. pole   13. stone   15. ill

12. bag   14. pile   16. treat

Word Play

Change Numbers to Letters
Use the code below to help you write six Core Words.

Number	1	2	3	4	5	6	7	8	9	10
Code	a	c	d	i	k	l	o	p	s	t

1. 6-7-2-5

2. 9-4-2-5

3. 9-10-4-2-5

4. 5-4-2-5

5. 9-10-1-2-5

6. 8-1-2-5

Read and Write
Write the Core Words that fit each clue.

7-9. Three words that begin with two consonants.

10-13. Four words that have a short *a* sound.

14-16. Three words that have a short *o* sound.

17-18. Two words that begin like

WRITE ON YOUR OWN

Make a list of things you like to do after school. Use three Core Words from this lesson.

Prooofreding prakticee
a ... c

1–3. Here is one student's list. Find three misspelled words. Write them correctly.

Things I Like to Do

1. Kik a football.
2. Hit a ball with a stik.
3. Fish off the dok.
4. Climb a rock.

Now proofread your list and correct any mistakes.

CORE		CHALLENGE
rock	sick	click
kick	stack	flock
sack	lock	shack
dock	stick	clock
pack	snack	backpack

5 Spelling the /nd/ and /st/ Sounds

FOCUS

CORE

1. sand
2. pond
3. lost
4. just
5. and
6. last
7. list
8. band
9. fast
10. hand

CHALLENGE

11. cast
12. stand
13. past
14. wind
15. land

Sound	Spelling
/nd/	ha**nd**
/st/	lo**st**

Say each word. Listen for the last sound you hear in *hand* and *lost*.

Study the spelling. How are these sounds spelled?

Write the words.
  1–10. Write the ten Core Words. Ring the letters that spell the last sounds.

  11–15. Write the five Challenge Words. Ring the letters that spell the last sounds.

SPELLING TIP
The /nd/ and /st/ sounds are spelled *nd* and *st*.

Complete the story with Core Words.

My Lost Cat

Fluffy is my pet cat. I cannot find her anywhere. She is <u>(1)</u>. I saw her <u>(2)</u> this morning after breakfast. Fluffy and I were near the frog <u>(3)</u> in my backyard. I was digging in the <u>(4)</u>. She was sitting next to me looking around.

I held out my <u>(5)</u>. "Here, Fluffy!" I called. But she ran away as <u>(6)</u> as she could. Maybe she saw another cat or a dog or a mouse! That was the <u>(7)</u> time I saw her.

She has a white <u>(8)</u> around her neck. She has white paws <u>(9)</u> a white tail. I made a <u>(10)</u> of places to look for her. I hope that I will find her soon. I miss my pet!

Words that Describe

Write the Core Words that the describing words tell something about.

11. big, loud

12. hot, white

13. cold, closed

14. deep, small

Make New Words

Take the first two letters and the last two letters of each word to make the Core Word. For example: <u>sa</u>lt + wi<u>nd</u> = sand

1. pool + land =

2. life + mist =

3. love + fist =

4. hall + kind =

5. fair + rust =

Listen to the Sounds

Write the Core Word that begins with the same sound as each picture name.

6.

7.

8.

9.

10.

Keep Looking

Write the Core Word that you find in each of these words.

11. unjust

12. breakfast

13. grand

14. listless

15. everlasting

Make a poster telling about something that you lost. You might tell what it looks like. Use three Core Words from this lesson.

Proofreding prakticee
a   c

1–3. Here is one student's poster. Three words are spelled wrong. Write each word correctly.

> **PLEASE HELP!**
> Have you seen Toby He is lawst. He is a brown and white horse. He has a white bandd down his back. Toby was last seen near the pend.

4. One question mark is missing at the end of a question. Copy the poster and correct the mistakes.

Now proofread your poster and correct any mistakes.

CORE		CHALLENGE
sand	last	cast
pond	list	stand
lost	band	past
just	fast	wind
and	hand	land

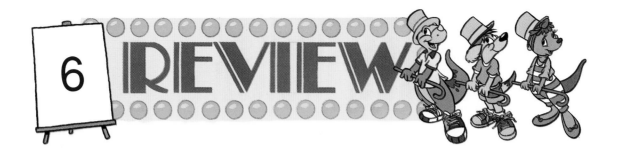

6 REVIEW

Write a Core Word from Lesson 1 for each clue below.

1. It makes a car run.
2. You put this on your head.
3. You can find your town on this.

Write a Core Word from Lesson 2 that fits each group of words.

4. hug, wave, hello, good-bye, ___
5. juice, water, tea, ___
6. hers, yours, mine, theirs, ___

Write a Core Word from Lesson 3 to complete each sentence. The missing word will rhyme with the underlined word.

7. An oven or fire is a <u>hot</u> ___ .
8. A pig who "barks" is a <u>hog</u> ___ .
9. When you have a little, you do <u>not</u> have a ___ .

REVIEW

Write a Core Word from Lesson 4 to complete each sentence.

10. Sara doesn't feel well. She feels ___.
11. The best after school ___ is an apple.
12. Miguel put one block on top of the other. He made a ___.

Write a Core Word from Lesson 5 that is the opposite of each word below.

13. found
14. first
15. slow

7 Spelling the Short *e* Sound

FOCUS

CORE

1. egg
2. fed
3. met
4. them
5. rest
6. bend
7. yet
8. test
9. went
10. send

CHALLENGE

11. pen
12. mess
13. stem
14. mend
15. west

Sound	Sign	Spelling
short *e*	/e/	fed

Say each word. Listen for the short *e* sound in *fed*.

Study the spelling. How is the vowel sound spelled?

Write the words.
  1–10. Write the ten Core Words. Ring the letter that spells the short *e* sound.

  11–15. Write the five Challenge Words. Ring the letter that spells the short *e* sound.

SPELLING TIP
The short *e* sound is often spelled *e*.

Words and Meanings

Complete the letter with Core Words.

Dear Uncle Bill

Dear Uncle Bill,

The other day I watched a robin build a nest. After the mother bird sat in it a while, a tiny (1) hatched. The baby robin poked its head out and (2) its mother.

The mother robin did not sit and (3). She (4) away to find food. Then she came back and (5) the baby a worm. She had to (6) way down to feed it.

Of course, the baby robin cannot leave the nest (7). Some day it will (8) its wings and try to fly.

I drew a picture of (9). I will (10) it to you. Will you come here soon to see the robins and their nest?

Love,
Molly

Past Tense

Add **-ed** to each word to show the past.
Now I pick. A day ago I picked.

11. rest   13. spell   15. peck
12. test   14. rent

Spell the Shapes

Use each of the shapes to help you spell the Core Words. Ring the three words that end with two consonants.

● = r　▲ = m　■ = h　▽ = s

■ = t　⇧ = n　◆ = d　⬇ = e

1. ▲⬇■

2. ■⬇▽■

3. ▽⬇⇧◆

4. ■■⬇▲

5. ●⬇▽■

Use the Dictionary

Where would you look to find these six Core Words in the dictionary? Use the chart below to help you.

went　met　egg　fed　yet　bend

abcdefghi	jklmnopq	rstuvwxyz
look in the beginning	look in the middle	look at the end

6. Which three words are found at the beginning of the dictionary?

7. Which word is found in the middle?

8. Which two words are found at the end of the dictionary?

WRITE ON YOUR OWN

Do you see birds near your house or on the way to school? Write a poem about birds. Use three Core Words from this lesson.

Proofreding prakticee

1–3. Here is one student's poem. Three words are spelled wrong. Write each word correctly.

I mat some little bluejays,
So I gave tham all some hay.
They built a small and cozy nest.
They worked hard and did not rist!

Now proofread your own poem and correct any mistakes.

CORE		CHALLENGE
egg	bend	pen
fed	yet	mess
met	test	stem
them	went	mend
rest	send	west

Spelling the Short *u* Sound

CORE

1. us
2. mud
3. rub
4. tug
5. luck
6. must
7. rug
8. shut
9. rust
10. stuck

CHALLENGE

11. dust
12. hush
13. lunch
14. rush
15. bunch

Sound	Sign	Spelling
short *u*	/u/	mud

Say each word. Listen for the short *u* sound in *mud*.

Study the spelling. How is the vowel sound spelled?

Write the words.

1–10. Write the ten Core Words. Ring the letter that spells the short *u* sound.

11–15. Write the five Challenge Words. Ring the letter that spells the short *u* sound.

SPELLING TIP
The short *u* sound is often spelled *u*.

Words and Meanings

Complete the story with Core Words.

Car Wash

Every Saturday I (1) wash our family car. My little sister helps me. We wash off the dirt and (2). We try not to get the inside of the car wet. We always make sure to (3) the windows before we wash it. Sometimes we find some (4) on the hood. But we cannot (5) it off with a rag.

After we wash the car, we shake the sand from the (6) on the floor. Sometimes the seat gets (7). One good (8) is all it takes to move it.

With (9) we can finish the job in an hour. It makes (10) feel good when the job is done. The car looks good, too!

Word Meaning

Write the Core Words that mean the same or almost the same as each word below.

11. dirt   13. close   15. carpet

12. pull   14. we   16. scrub

Ring the Words

Write the word in each sentence that has the Core Word hidden in it. Then ring the Core Word.

1. You can see a tugboat in the harbor.
2. There are many rubber boots in the store.
3. I will go on the bus with my friend.
4. They are shutting the windows.
5. We are lucky to be such good friends.

Break the Code

Use ABC order to fill in the missing letter in each group. Then write the Core Word that is spelled with the underlined letters.

$$s \; \underline{t} \; u \quad t \; \underline{u} \; v \quad f \; \underline{g} \; h \; = \; tug$$

6. r ___ t   s ___ u   t ___ v   b ___ d   j ___ l
7. q ___ s   t ___ v   r ___ t   s ___ u
8. l ___ n   t ___ v   c ___ e
9. q ___ s   t ___ v   f ___ h
10. l ___ n   t ___ v   r ___ t   s ___ u

Rhyme and Spell

Write two Core Words that rhyme with each word below.

11–12. duck   **13–14.** bug   **15–16.** dust

WRITE ON YOUR OWN

Have you ever cleaned a car? Write your own directions describing the things you should do. Use three Core Words from this lesson.

Prooofreding prakticee
(a) (c)

1–3. Here is one student's directions. Three words are spelled wrong. Write each word correctly.

1. Shet the doors and close the windows.
2. Wash the car and rob with a rag.
3. Shake the dirt from the rog.

Now proofread your own directions and correct any mistakes.

CORE		CHALLENGE
us	must	dust
mud	rug	hush
rub	shut	lunch
tug	rust	rush
luck	stuck	bunch

9 Spelling Words with *dr*, *tr*, and *gr*

FOCUS

CORE

1. drip
2. grin
3. tree
4. drum
5. grade
6. trip
7. drive
8. grand
9. truck
10. drove

CHALLENGE

11. dress
12. trim
13. grass
14. try
15. grow

Sound	Spelling
/dr/	**dr**ive
/tr/	**tr**uck
/gr/	**gr**ade

Say each word. Listen for the first two sounds in *drive*, *truck*, and *grade*.

Study the spelling. How are the first two sounds spelled?

Write the words.

1–10. Write *dr*, *tr*, and *gr* on the top of your paper. Write the Core Words that belong under each consonant blend.

11–15. Write the five Challenge Words. Ring the letters that spell the beginning sounds.

SPELLING TIP
The /dr/, /tr/, and /gr/ sounds are spelled *dr*, *tr*, and *gr*.

WORDS and MEANINGS

Complete the story with Core Words.

The Family Truck

Mal is in the second (1). His family owns a gray pickup (2). They park it on the driveway under a shady (3).

One day oil began to (4) from it. So the truck had to be taken to be fixed. It is still a (5) truck. Mal likes to ride in it. One day when he is older, Mal wants to (6) a truck just like it.

Last summer Mal went with his family on a (7). They (8) a long way to see some friends. Their friends gave Mal a present when he got there. They knew that Mal likes music so they gave him a big (9). Mal gave them a big (10) in return. He was so happy with his surprise!

Word Endings

Each word below has an ending. Write the Core Word you find in each word.

11. dripped
12. trees

13. grinning
14. trucker

15. drummers
16. grades

Figure It Out Write the Core Word that is spelled after you add and subtract letters.

1. grove - gr + dr =
2. land - l + gr =
3. sip - s + tr =
4. win - w + gr =
5. ship - sh + dr =

Think and Write Write a Core Word for each clue below.

6. Someone might tell you to beat it.
7. It could go from ear to ear.
8. You cannot hear its bark, but you can see it.
9. You need a car before you can do this.
10. An "A" is a good one.

Be an Author Write the missing Core Word in each book title. Be sure to start with a capital letter.

11.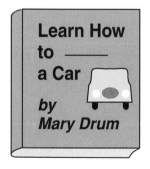
Learn How to ___ a Car

by
Mary Drum

12.
Maps for ___ Drivers

by
Stan Grand

13.
How to Have a ___ Time

by
Beth Trip

Follow the steps on pages 134–135 to write a story about a trip you have taken. Use three Core Words from this lesson.

Proofreding prakticee

1–3. Here is one student's story. Three words are spelled wrong. Write each word correctly.

> Last summer my family took a trap. we had a grond time. We drov to the lake. it was a long drive, but we had lots of fun.

4–5. Two capital letters were not used at the beginning of sentences. Copy the story and correct all mistakes.

Now proofread your own story and correct any mistakes.

CORE		CHALLENGE
drip	trip	dress
grin	drive	trim
tree	grand	grass
drum	truck	try
grade	drove	grow

10 Spelling Words with *gl*, *bl*, and *pl*

FOCUS

CORE

1. blast
2. glad
3. plan
4. blend
5. plus
6. glass
7. plum
8. blink
9. plot
10. block

CHALLENGE

11. glue
12. blank
13. planet
14. gloves
15. blanket

Sound	Spelling
/gl/	**gl**ad
/bl/	**bl**ast
/pl/	**pl**um

Say each word. Listen for the first two sounds in *glad*, *blast*, and *plum*.

Study the spelling. How are the first two sounds spelled?

Write the words.

1–10. Write *gl*, *bl*, and *pl* on the top of your paper. Write the Core Words that belong under each consonant blend.

11–15. Write the five Challenge Words. Ring the letters that spell the beginning sounds.

SPELLING TIP
The /gl/, /bl/, and /pl/ sounds are spelled *gl*, *bl*, and *pl*.

Dear Jake

Complete the letter with Core Words.

Dear Jake,

We (1) to have a picnic on the Fourth of July. I am very (2). Everyone on our (3) will come. My family will bring (4) pudding. We will also bring a (5) of punch for everyone. We will (6) apple and pear juice to make it.

Our town will have fireworks that night. The show will be held on a big (7) of land. We will watch the fireworks (8) off. If you (9) you'll miss them!

Fireworks (10) a picnic will add up to a good time for all. I hope you can come to our block party.

> Your friend,
> Becky

More Than One

Add **-es** to words ending with **-s** to show more than one.

glass   glasses

11. one dress, two ___

12. one boss, three ___

13. one plus, four ___

14. one class, six ___

15. one mess, five ___

16. one gas, nine ___

Picture the Words Write Core Words to answer each question.

1–4. Which words have the same beginning sounds as

5–8. Which words have the same beginning sounds as

9–10. Which words have the same beginning sounds as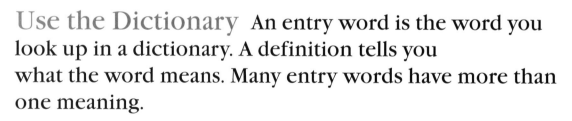

Use the Dictionary An entry word is the word you look up in a dictionary. A definition tells you what the word means. Many entry words have more than one meaning.

Look up the word *plot* in your Speller Dictionary to answer the questions.

11. What is the entry word?
12. What is the second meaning?
13. What is the sentence given for the first meaning?
14. Which meaning is *the main idea of a book?*
15. Which two Core Words came after *plot?*

Write an invitation to a friend for a Fourth of July picnic. Use three Core Words from this lesson.

1–3. Here is one student's invitation. Three words are spelled wrong. Write each word correctly.

> Please plain to come to our picnic on the
> Fourth of July. I will be so glod We will have
> food plas games

4–5. Two periods were not put in at the end of sentences. Copy the invitation and correct all mistakes.

Now proofread your own invitations and correct any mistakes.

CORE		CHALLENGE
blast	glass	glue
glad	plum	blank
plan	blink	planet
blend	plot	gloves
plus	block	blanket

11 Spelling Words That End with *sk*, *mp*, and *ng*

FOCUS

CORE

1. mask
2. camp
3. long
4. ask
5. sting
6. dump
7. wing
8. desk
9. song
10. jump

CHALLENGE

11. blimp
12. task
13. stamp
14. bring
15. grump

Sound	Spelling
/sk/	ma**sk**
/mp/	ca**mp**
/ng/	wi**ng**

Say each word. Listen for the ending sounds in *mask*, *camp*, and *wing*.

Study the spelling. How are the ending sounds spelled?

Write the words.

1–3. Write the three Core Words that end with *sk*.

4–6. Write the three Core Words that end with *mp*.

7–10. Write the four Core Words that end with *ng*.

11–15. Write the five Challenge Words. Ring the letters that spell the ending sounds.

SPELLING TIP

The /sk/, /mp/, and /ng/ sounds are spelled *sk*, *mp*, and *ng*.

WORDS and MEANINGS

Complete the checklist with Core Words.

Things to Do

When you (1) in the woods, there are some things you must remember to do. Here is a list I wrote at my (2).

1. Be sure to (3) someone where you can put your tent.
2. Bugs may (4), so bring a spray.
3. Take a (5) walk every day.
4. Look for a blackbird with red feathers on its (6).
5. When you spot a raccoon, look for the (7) that seems to be on its face.
6. Watch a frog (8) over a log.
7. Sing a happy camp (9) every evening.
8. Remember to (10) your trash in a can before you leave.

Adding -ing

Add **-ing** to the end of each Core Word.

bring + ing = bringing

11. camp
12. dump
13. sting
14. jump
15. ask

Finish the Rhyme Write the Core Word that rhymes with each underlined word.

1. Put a <u>stamp</u> on the letter to ___.
2. Why did you toss the <u>pump</u> in the ___?
3. We sang a <u>song</u> that was too ___.
4. Please <u>ask</u> them if they have a ___.
5. When the car went over the <u>bump</u> it made me ___.

Compare and Write Write the missing Core Word that finishes the sentences.

6. A fish has a fin. A bird has a ___.

7. A rabbit can hop. A frog can ___.

8. An artist paints a picture. A singer sings a ___.

9. A snake can bite. A bee can ___.

10. A teacher can write on a chalkboard.
    A student can write at a ___.

Ask and Tell Read each pair of sentences. Write the word *ask* if the sentence is a question. Write the word *tell* if the sentence gives an answer.

11. What is wrong with that bird?
12. I think it has a broken wing.
13. My desk is near the window.
14. Where is your desk in the classroom?

Have you ever gone to summer camp or camping with your family. Write some rules for camping. Use three Core Words from this lesson.

Proofreding prakticee

1–4. Here are one student's rules. Four words are spelled wrong. Write each word correctly.

1. Do not junp on the bed.
2. Take your trash to the domp.
3. Write a log letter home every week.
4. Get help for a bee steng.

Now proofread your own rules and correct any mistakes.

CORE		CHALLENGE
mask	dump	blimp
camp	wing	task
long	desk	stamp
ask	song	bring
sting	jump	grump

12 REVIEW

Write a Core Word from Lesson 7 to complete each sentence.

1. Roger is still not here. He hasn't come ___.
2. Each chicken has an ___ in its nest.
3. Amber got a good grade on the spelling ___.

Write a Core Word from Lesson 8 for each meaning below.

4. wet dirt
5. a cover for a floor
6. cannot move

Write a Core Word from Lesson 9 that fits each group of words below.

7. bark, leaf, trunk, ___
8. car, van, bus, ___
9. horn, piano, guitar, ___

Write the sentences below. Replace the underlined word with a Core Word from Lesson 10.

10. Mary was <u>happy</u> that Mona could come to the party.
11. First put in the milk, then <u>mix</u> in the eggs.
12. Three <u>and</u> three equals six.

Write a Core Word from Lesson 11 to finish each sentence. The missing word will rhyme with the underlined word.

13. It rained on our tents.
    Now we have a <u>damp</u> ___.
14. Don't play that music.
    That is the <u>wrong</u> ___.
15. The bird had a <u>string</u> caught on its ___.

13 Spelling the Long a Sound

FOCUS

CORE

1. rake
2. bait
3. say
4. cane
5. pail
6. hay
7. plate
8. raise
9. came
10. grape

CHALLENGE

11. trail
12. blaze
13. pain
14. tray
15. stain

Sound	Sign	Spelling
long *a*	/ā/	rake bait hay

Say each word. Listen for the long *a* sound in *rake, bait,* and *hay.*

Study the spelling. How is the long *a* sound spelled in each word?

Write the words.

1–10. Write the ten Core Words. Ring the letters that spell the long *a* sound.

11–15. Write the five Challenge Words. Ring the letters that spell the long *a* sound.

SPELLING TIP

The long *a* sound can be spelled *a-e, ai,* and *ay.*

Words and Meanings

Complete the story with Core Words.

Gone Fishing

My friend and I like to fish. We made our own fishing rods. We used an old walking (1) for one fishing rod. For the other rod, we used the handle of an old garden (2). It had been used to gather grass and (3). We use worms for (4).

Some days we have no fish to carry home in our (5). But I would (6) that we are lucky most of the time. When we (7) the fishing line out of the water, a fish is usually on the hook.

One day we (8) home with ten fish. At supper, two fresh fish were on each (9). They tasted great with some vegetables, rice, and (10) juice.

Same Sound, Different Meaning

Write the two words in each group with the same sound but different spellings and meanings.

11. pail, pale, peal
12. tall, tail, tale
13. hey, hi, hay
14. hole, hold, whole
15. plain, plan, plane

Picture This Scene
Write the six Core Words you can find in the picture.

1-6.

Write the Rhyme
Write the Core Words that rhyme with each word.

7. drape
8. bake
9. wait
10. pay
11. game
12. gate
13. mail
14. lane

Use the Dictionary
Entry words in the dictionary are in ABC order. When entry words begin with the same letter, you must look at the second letter. Write the words in each group in the order you would find them in the dictionary.

15. plate   pole   pail
16. came   crane   clay
17. rust   raise   reel
18. coat   cane   crab

Have you ever caught a fish? Follow the steps on pages 134–135 to write a newspaper story about fishing. Use three Core Words from this lesson.

Prooofreding prakticee

1–4. Here is one student's newspaper story. Four words are spelled wrong. Write each word correctly.

> Yesterday two big fish were caught off the town
> dock Worms were used for bate The fish were so
> big they could not fit on a dinner plat. Many people
> kame to see them. Some sey they were the biggest
> fish they have ever seen!

5–6. Two periods were not put in at the ends of sentences. Copy the story and correct all mistakes.

Now proofread your own newspaper story and correct any mistakes.

CORE		CHALLENGE
rake	hay	trail
bait	plate	blaze
say	raise	pain
cane	came	tray
pail	grape	stain

14 Spelling the Long e Sound

CORE

1. read
2. each
3. seen
4. wheel
5. team
6. deep
7. meal
8. treat
9. dream
10. sheep

CHALLENGE

11. mean
12. cream
13. sneeze
14. leave
15. sleep

Sound	Sign	Spelling
long e	/ē/	meal seen

Say each word. Listen for the long e sound in *meal* and *seen*.

Study the spelling. How is the long e sound spelled in each Core Word?

Write the words.

1–10. Write the ten Core Words. Ring the two letters that spell the long e sound.

11–15. Write the five Challenge Words. Ring the two letters that spell the long e sound.

SPELLING TIP

The long e sound can be spelled *ea* and *ee*.

WORDS and MEANINGS

Complete the story with Core Words.

Dreamland

Do you like to <u>(1)</u> books? I like make-believe stories the best. One night I fell into a <u>(2)</u> sleep. I had a strange <u>(3)</u>. I dreamed about a girl and boy in one of the books.

The girl and boy had to watch over a herd of <u>(4)</u> all the time. They found a surprise late one day when they were about to eat their evening <u>(5)</u>. It was a real <u>(6)</u>!

They found out that <u>(7)</u> bean on their dinner plates was magic! Every bean became a <u>(8)</u> that went around and around! On top of the wheels was a beautiful coach. It was pulled by a <u>(9)</u> of white horses.

The girl and boy climbed into the coach and rode into the sky, laughing. They were never <u>(10)</u> again.

Same Spelling, Different Meaning

Write the word that fits the two meanings below.

beat   seal   deep   meal

11. breakfast/ ground corn
12. animal/close an envelope
13. hit again/mix together
14. far down/rich in color

Unscramble the Words
Unscramble and write the three Core Words in the poem.

1–3. Try to reda a book chae and every day,
A few pages at a time will get you on your way.
Many new friends you will surely meet,
It will be a lot of fun and a real eattr!

Write a Hink Pink
Write the Core Word that answers the question and rhymes with the underlined word.

4. What is a round hub? a <u>steel</u> ___

5. What is a very long nap? a ___ <u>sleep</u>

6. What is lunch for a sea animal? a <u>seal</u> ___

7. What is a winning sports group? a ___ <u>team</u>

Look in All Directions
Write the six Core Words you find hidden in the letter square.

8–13.

S	V	W	X	A	D
E	T	E	A	M	E
E	E	A	C	H	E
N	S	H	E	E	P
D	R	E	A	M	W

Do you have a favorite book? Tell about the book and why you like the story. Use three Core Words from this lesson.

Proofreding prakticee

1-3. Here is one student's book report. Three words are spelled wrong. Write each word correctly.

> My favorite book is about shep. They live on a big farm. I red some pages ech day. It helps me learn about animals and how to treat them.

Now proofread your own book report and correct any mistakes.

CORE		CHALLENGE
read	deep	mean
each	meal	cream
seen	treat	sneeze
wheel	dream	leave
team	sheep	sleep

15 Spelling the Long *i* Sound

CORE

1. pine
2. night
3. cry
4. fight
5. wide
6. fly
7. light
8. sight
9. dry
10. right

CHALLENGE

11. sly
12. might
13. stripe
14. shy
15. tight

FOCUS

Sound	Sign	Spelling
long *i*	/ī/	wid**e** dr**y** n**igh**t

Say each word. Listen for the long *i* sound in *wide*, *dry*, and *night*.

Study the spelling. How is the long *i* sound spelled in each Core Word?

Write the words.

1-10. Write the ten Core Words. Ring the letters in each word that spell the long *i* sound.

11–15. Write the five Challenge Words. Ring the letters that spell the long *i* sound.

SPELLING TIP

The long *i* sound can be spelled *i-e*, *y*, and *igh*.

WORDS and MEANINGS

Complete the letter with Core Words.

Dear Tony

Dear Tony,

Do you want to go for a plane ride with me? In the daytime, we will see many things because it is (1). We can (2) over houses and trees. We will soar over the long, (3) river below us. We will swoop low over a (4) forest. At (5), we will see the moon and the stars and the city lights.

We will take turns sitting near the window. That way we will not (6) over the seat. Do not get scared and (7) if the ride gets bumpy. Just (8) your eyes. Look to both the left and (9). I know you will enjoy each wonderful (10)!

Your pal,
Julie

Opposites

Write the Core Word that means the opposite of each word below.

11. day	13. wet	15. laugh
12. left	14. narrow	16. heavy

Finish the Signs
Write the Core Word that completes each sign.

1-2. Do not _____ your kite at _____ .

3-4. All _____ trucks keep to the _____ .

5-6. Turn on the _____ to help your _____ .

7-8. Do not climb _____ without _____ boots.

9. Children should share their toys rather than _____ .

Write the Words
Write the Core Words that fit the descriptions.

10–12. Which three words end with long *i* spelled *y?*

13–14. Which two words end with vowel-consonant-vowel?

Use the Dictionary
Many words have more than one meaning. A dictionary lists all the meanings for a word. Read the pairs of meanings. Write the Core Word that fits both meanings.

15. an insect with two wings; move through the air
16. a lamp; not dark
17. good or correct; opposite of left
18. kind of tree; wish or long for something

Pilots always listen to weather reports. What is today's weather? Write a weather report. Use three Core Words from this lesson.

Prooofreding prakticee

(editorial marks: a above "Prooofreding"; c above "prakticee"; deletion and capitalization marks)

1–4. Here is one student's report. Four words are spelled wrong. Write each word correctly.

> today will be fair and dri. clouds will move in at nit. It will rain rite after midnight. pilots should not flie their planes. Stay at home until the sky clears!

5–7. Three sentences do not begin with capital letters. Copy the weather report and correct all mistakes.

Now proofread your own weather report and correct any mistakes.

CORE		CHALLENGE
pine	fly	sly
night	light	might
cry	sight	stripe
fight	dry	shy
wide	right	tight

16 Spelling the Long *o* Sound

CORE

1. coat
2. blow
3. nose
4. boat
5. row
6. those
7. goat
8. soap
9. snow
10. toad

CHALLENGE

11. slow
12. coach
13. float
14. globe
15. toast

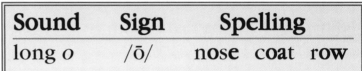

FOCUS

Sound	Sign	Spelling
long *o*	/ō/	n**o**s**e** c**oa**t r**ow**

Say each word. Listen for the long *o* sound in *nose*, *coat*, and *row*.

Study the spelling. How is the long *o* sound spelled in each word?

Write the words.

1–10. Write the ten Core Words. Ring the letters that spell the long *o* sound.

11–15. Write the five Challenge Words. Ring the letters that spell the long *o* sound.

SPELLING TIP

The long *o* sound can be spelled *o-e*, *oa*, and *ow*.

WORDS and MEANINGS

Complete the report with Core Words.

Up in the Mountains

This report is about an animal called the mountain (1). It leaps from rock to rock like a (2) jumping from log to log. It races over the hills like a (3) gliding over water. It can even cling to the side of a cliff with (4) strong hooves. It would be as hard to catch as a wet bar of (5).

Ice and (6) often cover the rocks of its home. Sometimes a cold wind will (7). It has a thick (8) of fur to keep it warm.

The mountain goat has to

poke its (9) around to find plants to eat. If it is lucky, it will find a (10) of moss on the hillside.

Compound Words

Add each word to the Core Word to make a compound word. Write the new word.

11. sail + boat =   13. rain + coat =   15. toad + stool =

12. nose + dive =   14. snow + ball =   16. soap + suds =

Pair Them Up Write the two missing Core Words in each sentence. Use the picture clues to help you.

1-2. Here is a ___
in a ___.

5-6. There is ___
on the ___.

3-4. This is a ___
you can ___.

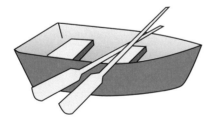

Think and Write Write Core Words for each clue.

7-9. three words that end with a long *o* sound

10-11. two words that end with the first sound you hear in *zebra*

12. the shortest word

Why are the mountains fun to visit? Write an ad for a trip to the mountains. Be sure to tell some things you can do there. Use three Core Words from this lesson.

Proofreding prakticee

1–3. Here is one student's ad. Four words are spelled wrong. Write each word correctly.

> In summer, roe a boat or go hiking. Perhaps you will see a mountain gote or a toad. In winter, play in the snoe. Then sit by the fire when the night winds bloo.

Proofread your own ad and correct any mistakes.

CORE		CHALLENGE
coat	those	slow
blow	goat	coach
nose	soap	float
boat	snow	globe
row	toad	toast

17 Spelling the /ü/ Sound

CORE

1. tube
2. zoo
3. boot
4. food
5. tune
6. pool
7. soon
8. rude
9. moon
10. room

CHALLENGE

11. moose
12. cute
13. balloon
14. shoot
15. goose

Sound	Spelling
/ü/	tune moon

Say each word. Listen for the /ü/ sound in *tune* and *moon*. Note the sign for this sound.

Study the spelling. How is the /ü/ sound spelled in each word?

Write the words.

1-10. Write the ten Core Words. Ring the two letters in each word that spell the vowel sound.

11-15. Write the five Challenge Words. Ring the two letters in each word that spell the /ü/ sound.

SPELLING TIP
The /ü/ sound can be spelled *u-e* and *oo*.

WORDS and MEANINGS

Complete the story with Core Words.

A Fun Place to Visit

Have you ever gone to the (1) to see the animals there? You can watch the seals swim in a (2). They have a lot of (3) to swim and dive. They like to play with a ball and an old tire (4). Sometimes they will clap their flippers if someone plays them a (5).

Every day at noon, the animal trainer gives them (6). Sometimes a big seal will take fish from a little seal. Do you think that is (7)?

If you stay until night, you will see the (8). But you must go home (9). If not, a zoo keeper might (10) you out!

Place Words

Town and *room* are words that name places. Write the place word in each group.

11. pool, boot, soon
12. tune, zoo, paper
13. food, room, clock

14. house, glove, table
15. stool, park, rude
16. June, lake, tube

Think and Write   Write the Core Word that is missing from each sentence.

1. *Person* is to *neighborhood* as *animal* is to ___.
2. *Head* is to *hat* as *foot* is to ___.
3. *Day* is to *sun* as *night* is to ___.
4. *Skate* is to *ice* as *swim* is to ___.
5. *Book* is to *words* as *song* is to ___.
6. *Drink* is to *water* as *eat* is to ___.

Be a News Reporter   Write the missing Core Word that finishes each newspaper headline. Be sure to begin each word with a capital letter.

7. TOWN TO GET A NEW SWIMMING ___

8. SPACESHIP LANDS ON THE ___

9. HUNGRY PEOPLE GET ___

10. PANDA BEAR GIVEN TO THE ___

Use the Dictionary   Write each set of entry words in the order you find them in the dictionary.

11. rude   room   rail   14. tube   trip   take
12. stem   soon   sun   15. zoo   zebra   zero
13. moon   mule   mean

What questions would you ask a zoo keeper?
Write a list of questions about working in a
zoo. Use three Core Words from this lesson.

Prooofreding prakticee

1–3. Here are one student's questions. Three words
are spelled wrong. Write each word correctly.

1. Do you like working at the zu?

2. What fod do you feed the lions.

3. How often do you clean the seal poole.

4–5. Two question marks were not put in at the
ends of questions. Copy the questions and
correct all mistakes.

Proofread your own questions and correct any
mistakes.

CORE		CHALLENGE
tube	pool	moose
zoo	soon	cute
boot	rude	balloon
food	moon	shoot
tune	room	goose

Write a Core Word from Lesson 13 to complete each sentence.

1. Lan used worms for ___ and caught six fish.
2. Your grandmother is here. Please ___ hello.
3. Meg piled the food on her ___.

Write a Core Word from Lesson 14 to complete each sentence. The missing word will rhyme with the underlined word.

4. A great rest is a ___ <u>sleep</u>.
5. A ten-cent lunch is a <u>deal</u> on a ___.
6. Cold lemonade on a hot day is a ___ in the <u>heat</u>.

Write a Core Word from Lesson 15 that means the opposite of each word below.

7. wet
8. wrong
9. day

REVIEW

Write a Core Word from Lesson 16 for each clue below.

10. This is used in the shower.
11. This is what the wind does.
12. This is part of the face.

Write a Core Word from Lesson 17 that fits each group of words below.

13. sun, stars, ___
14. bear, lion, tiger, ___
15. music, song, ___

19 Spelling Words with *wh* and *sh*

FOCUS

CORE

1. what
2. clash
3. shame
4. why
5. shine
6. flash
7. shock
8. where
9. shore
10. while

CHALLENGE

11. whisper
12. shall
13. share
14. whiskers
15. shadow

Sound	Spelling
/hw/ or /w/	**wh**at
/sh/	**sh**ine fla**sh**

Say each word. Listen for the first sound you hear in *what*. Listen for the last sound you hear in *flash*. Note the signs for these sounds.

Study the spelling. How are these sounds spelled in the Core Words?

Write the words.

1–4. Write the four Core Words with the /hw/ or /w/ sound spelled *wh*.

5–10. Write the six Core Words with the /sh/ sound spelled *sh*.

11–15. Write the five Challenge Words. Ring the letters that spell the /hw/, /w/, or /sh/ sounds.

SPELLING TIP
The /hw/ or /w/ sound is often spelled *wh*.
The /sh/ sound is often spelled *sh*.

Complete the story with Core Words.

OUR SCHOOL BAND

Can you guess the reason (1) I play in the school band? I love to hear the (2) of brass.

The places (3) we play are always different. Once we played as we marched along the (4) of a lake. It was lots of fun.

At first, the day was nice. We hoped the sun would (5) all day. Do you know (6) happened? It started to grow darker and darker. Then we saw a (7) of light! Soon after we heard claps of thunder.

The storm came as a (8) to all of us. We played (9) it rained. Our band leader said it was a (10) that we all got wet. I had fun clashing along with the thunder!

Compound Words
Add a Core Word to each word below. Write the compound word.

11. ___ + light

12. some + ___

13. sun + ___

14. ___ + ever

15. ___ + line

16. mean + ___

Lesson 19 69

Find a Rhyme
Write the Core Word that rhymes with the underlined word in each sentence.

1. Can you <u>smile</u> for a little ___ ?
2. I feel <u>fine</u> when the sun does ___ .
3. Is there a book <u>store</u> near the sea ___ ?
4. When I fell off the <u>rock</u>, it was a big ___ .

Look and Spell
Write the Core Words that answer the questions.

5–8. Which four words have the same beginning sound as ?

9–10. Which two words have the same final sound as  ?

11–14. Which four words have the same beginning sound as ?

Write the Questions
Write a question to go with each answer. Be sure to use *what, where*, or *why* in your question. Remember to end each question with a question mark. Ring each question word that you use.

15. Question: ___   Answer: They are at the shore.
16. Question: ___   Answer: We are looking for seashells.
17. Question: ___   Answer: We need the shells for the science fair.

WRITE ON YOUR OWN

What is your favorite song? Write some new words to a song you like, such as the birthday song. You might like to make a new song. Use three Core Words from this lesson.

Prooofreding prakticee

a c

1–3. Here are the words to one student's song. Three words are spelled wrong. Write each word correctly.

Oh, wy did you move?

Oh, wher are you now?

It is such a sham,

Nothing is the same without you.

Proofread your own song words. Correct any mistakes.

CORE		CHALLENGE
what	flash	whisper
clash	shock	shall
shame	where	share
why	shore	whiskers
shine	while	shadow

20 Spelling Words with *ch* and *th*

FOCUS

Sound	Spelling
/ch/	**ch**oke
/th/	**th**ank wi**th**

Say each word. Listen for the first sound you hear in *choke* and *thank*. Note the signs for these sounds.

Study the spelling. How are the /ch/ and /th/ sounds spelled in the Core Words?

Write the words.

1–4. Write the four Core Words spelled with *ch*.

5–10. Write the six Core Words spelled with *th*.

11–15. Write the five Challenge Words. Ring the letters that spell the /ch/ and /th/ sounds.

SPELLING TIP
The /ch/ and /th/ sounds are spelled *ch* and *th*.

CORE

1. much
2. thing
3. such
4. choke
5. tooth
6. thank
7. bath
8. thin
9. teach
10. with

CHALLENGE

11. child
12. thick
13. reach
14. chore
15. think

Growing Up

On Saturday I woke up (1) all my teeth in my mouth. But the (2) that would change that was an apple.

I had so (3) to do that day. First, I wanted to (4) my dog a new trick. While we were playing my dog ran into a big mud puddle. So I had to give it a (5). My dog did not (6) me after I was done!

Then I stopped for lunch. After eating my sandwich, I ate an apple. I try to eat every meal so I will not be too (7)!

All of a sudden, my (8) fell out when I bit into the apple.

It was (9) a surprise! I was lucky that I did not swallow my tooth and (10). I hope my new tooth will grow in soon!

Word Endings

Add **-er** to the end of each word to show *a person who.*

buy + er = buyer

11. teach   13. climb   15. speak
12. paint   14. catch

Finish the Puzzles

On a separate piece of paper, write the Core Words that fit each puzzle.

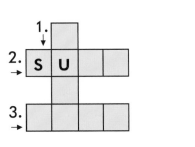

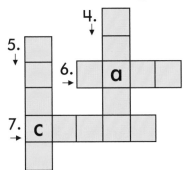

Hide and Seek

Write the Core Words hidden in each ad.

8.

Buy two toothbrushes. Get one free.

9.

THIS WEEK ONLY

All bathtubs on sale!

10.

A treat without a fuss! Try new snack bars.

Use the Dictionary

A dictionary entry often gives a sample sentence to help explain a word's meaning. Study How to Use a Dictionary on pages 136 and 137. Look up the Core Words below in the Speller Dictionary. Then write your own sentence for each of these Core Words.

11. teach   13. choke   15. thing

12. thank   14. bath

Have you ever lost a tooth? Write an entry in your diary. Use three Core Words from this lesson.

Proofreading practice

1–4. Here is one student's diary entry. Four words are spelled wrong. Write each word correctly.

> today I lost my front tuth. I was taking a bathe
> and playing whith my toys. suddenly it fell out. It
> was a strange thig to happen.

5–6. Two capital letters were not put in at the beginnings of sentences. Copy the diary entry and correct all mistakes.

Proofread your own diary entry. Correct any mistakes.

CORE		CHALLENGE
much	thank	child
thing	bath	thick
such	thin	reach
choke	teach	chore
tooth	with	think

21 Spelling the Vowel + *r* Sound

FOCUS

CORE

1. farm
2. cart
3. dark
4. yard
5. art
6. barn
7. park
8. start
9. hard
10. sharp

CHALLENGE

11. arm
12. march
13. alarm
14. smart
15. harm

Sound	Spelling
/är/	c**ar**t

Say each word. Listen for the vowel + *r* sound you hear in *cart*. Note the sign for this sound.

Study the spelling. How is the /är/ sound spelled in each Core Word?

Write the words.

  1–10. Write the ten Core Words. Ring the letters that spell the /är/ sound.

  11–15. Write the five Challenge Words. Ring the letters that spell the /är/ sound.

SPELLING TIP
The /är/ sound may be spelled *ar*.

Down on the Farm

My cousins live on a small (1). Like most farmers, they work very (2). They have to (3) their chores early. Just after sunrise, they fill a (4) with feed for the pigs. Then they head for the (5) to milk the cows. Sometimes they work until it is (6).

On the weekends there are chores to do around the house. They have to cut the grass in the front (7). Of course, if the blades on the mower are (8), the work goes faster.

Then they have time for some fun. Sometimes they like to go to the baseball (9) to watch the home team play. Other times they take painting lessons at (10) school. They always like to keep busy!

Comparing Things

The endings **-er** and **-est** are used to compare. Add **-er** and **-est** to each word in the chart.

11. sharp   13. dark   15. smart
12. short   14. long   16. hard

Word Play

Find and Change Write the Core Words that mean the opposite of the underlined words.

1. It is <u>easy</u> to learn to roller skate.
2. I painted the sky <u>light</u> blue in the picture.
3. The blade on the knife is <u>dull</u>.
4. When will the bus <u>stop</u>?

Answer the Riddle Write the Core Words that answer the riddles.

5. I am a building. I am red. Horses and cows live in me.
6. I am outside of a house or school.
   Sometimes children play on my grass.
7. I have wheels. I carry things.
8. I am land. People grow all kinds of crops on me.
9. I am a big open space where people like to picnic.
   I have grass and trees. Sometimes I am in the city.

Finish the Book Cover Write titles for books using the following Core Words: *art, farm, park.* Be sure to begin words in your book titles with capital letters.
10–12.

WRITE ON YOUR OWN

Have you ever visited a farm? What are some of the farmer's chores? Make a list of the things that farmers do. Use three Core Words from this lesson.

Prooofreding prakticee

1-3. Here is one student's list. Three words are spelled wrong. Write each word correctly.

Farm Chores

1. Clean the born.
2. Fill the carte with hay.
3. Rake the yerd.
4. Feed the cows.

Now proofread your own lists. Correct any mistakes.

CORE		CHALLENGE
farm	barn	arm
cart	park	march
dark	start	alarm
yard	hard	smart
art	sharp	harm

22 Spelling More Vowel + *r* Sounds

FOCUS

CORE

1. girl
2. more
3. bird
4. horse
5. dirt
6. horn
7. short
8. first
9. for
10. shirt

CHALLENGE

11. store
12. third
13. morning
14. dinosaur
15. whirl

Sound	Spelling
/ûr/	b**ir**d
/ôr/	h**or**n

Say each word. Listen for the vowel + *r* sound in *bird* and *girl*. Listen for the vowel + *r* sound in *horn* and *for*. Note the signs for these sounds.

Study the spelling. How are the /ûr/ and /ôr/ sounds spelled in each Core Word?

Write the words.

1–5. Write the five Core Words with the /ûr/ sound.

6–10. Write the five Core Words with the /ôr/ sound.

11–15. Write the five Challenge Words. Ring the letters that spell the /ûr/ and /ôr/ sounds.

SPELLING TIP

The /ûr/ sounds may be spelled *ir*.
The /ôr/ sounds may be spelled *or*.

WORDS and MEANINGS

Complete the story with Core Words.

Early One Morning

Sarah woke up very early one morning when she heard a car (1). Nobody in the house was awake yet.

The young (2) got out of bed quickly. She put on a pair of pants and a (3). She wanted to enjoy her (4) day of summer vacation.

Sarah went outside after she fixed herself some breakfast. A small brown (5) greeted her with a song. She headed (6) the barn. It was only a (7) walk away.

Inside the barn, her (8) was waiting in a stall. He dug his hoof in the (9) when he saw her. She fed him some hay. She would give him some (10) to eat later. Then she went riding.

Number Words

Number words tell *how many* and *which order*. Write the number word for each space.

third first fifth second fourth

11. the 1st bird, the ___ bird
12. the 2nd dog, the ___ dog
13. the 3rd cat, the ___ cat
14. the 4th pig, the ___ pig
15. the 5th fish, the ___ fish

Be a Magician
Take away one word from the letters in each box. Write the Core Word that is left.

1. Take away Find a farm animal. | horhayse |

2. Take away Find something in a band. | honotesrn |

3. Take away Find something that flies. | worbirdm |

4. Take away Find something to wear. | shiballrt |

5. Take away Find something to dig in. | dipailrt |

6. Take away Find a person. | gimaskrl |

Fill It In
Write the missing Core Word. Be sure to begin each word with a capital letter.

7. SALE — ___

8.  Prize

9.  Save Here!

10. 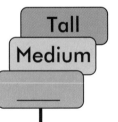 Tall / Medium / ___

Use the Dictionary
Many words have more than one meaning. Look up the word below in the Speller Dictionary. Write two sentences using *horn*. Each sentence must use a different meaning for *horn*.

11–12. horn

Write a plan for your activities for a summer morning. Be sure to tell the things you will be doing. Use three Core Words from this lesson.

Prooofreding praktice
(a) *(c)*

1–4. Here is one student's plan. Five words are spelled wrong. Write each word correctly.

8:00–9:00	Make breakfast fer my family.
9:00–10:00	Buy a new red shert.
10:00–11:00	Go for a ride on my hors.
11:00–noon	Repair the berd cage one mor time.

Proofread your own plan. Correct any mistakes.

CORE		**CHALLENGE**
girl	horn	store
more	short	third
bird	first	morning
horse	for	dinosaur
dirt	shirt	whirl

23 Easily Misspelled Words

FOCUS

CORE

1. does
2. gone
3. who
4. any
5. your
6. give
7. very
8. were
9. live
10. every

CHALLENGE

11. many
12. away
13. goes
14. kind
15. both

Say each word. Listen for the vowel and consonant sounds.

Study the spelling. Look for unusual or tricky spellings.

Write the words.

1–10. Write the ten Core Words. Ring any spellings you find unusual. Try to remember them.

11–15. Write the five Challenge Words. Ring any spellings you find unusual. Try to remember them.

SPELLING TIP
Some words do not follow common spelling patterns.

WORDS and MEANINGS

Complete the story with Core Words.

Road Race

Is there someone you know (1) likes to run? Maybe it is a friend or someone in (2) family. Maybe it is you! These days there are many people who are runners.

Running is a good way to keep fit. It (3) not matter if you (4) in the city or in the country. You can find a place to run (5) day.

Some day you might like to enter a race. Are there (6) races near where you live? Have you ever even (7) to a race? Some races are (8) long. Each runner has to go over 26 miles to reach the finish line. The runners have to (9) their best. How do you think you would feel if you (10) in such a long race?

Same Spelling, Different Word

Write a word from the box that fits both blanks in each sentence.

live   does   close   wind

11. ___ a door ___ to you.
12. I ___ near a ___ lion.
13. ___ the baby see the ___?
14. ___ a rope in the ___.

Add the Vowels
Write the Core Words that are spelled by filling in the missing vowels. Be sure to remember that the letter *y* is sometimes used as a vowel.

1. g __ n __
2. __ n __
3. w __ r __
4. g __ v __
5. d __ __ s

6. __ v __ r __
7. l __ v __
8. y __ __ r
9. wh __
10. v __ r __

Answer and Write
Write the Core Words that answer the questions.

11. Which word is a question word?
12. Which word has the word *very* in it?
13-15. Which three words end with a long *e* sound that is spelled *y?*

Find the Meaning
Write the Core Words that can be used in place of the underlined words in each sentence.

16. Teachers <u>hand over</u> books to their students.
17. I hope to read a book <u>each</u> week.
18. The child is <u>greatly</u> happy with the bike.
19. Would you like <u>some</u> grapes to eat?
20. The painter has <u>moved</u> from the city.

Write a postcard to a friend who has just won a race. Be sure to ask questions about the race. Use three Core Words from this lesson.

Pro͟ofreding prakticee
a c

1–4. Here is one student's postcard. Four words are spelled wrong. Write each word correctly.

Dear Alice,

I am vary happy you won the race. Did they giv you a medal Will you run in eny more races Wu came in second?

Your pal,

Nick

5–6. Two question marks were not put in at the ends of questions. Copy the postcard and correct all mistakes.

Now proofread your own postcard. Correct any mistakes.

CORE		CHALLENGE
does	give	many
gone	very	away
who	were	goes
any	live	kind
your	every	both

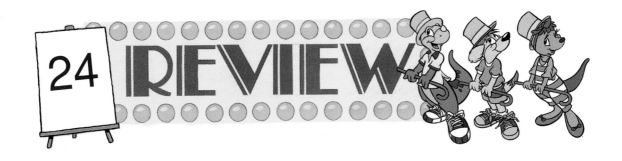

24 REVIEW

Write a Core Word from Lesson 19 for each clue below.

1. a question word that rhymes with *air*
2. a bright light that rhymes with *dash*
3. land that is next to a lake or sea that rhymes with *more*

Write a Core Word from Lesson 20 to fill the blank in each pair of sentences. The missing word will rhyme with the underlined word.

4. Ben adds numbers when he is in the tub.
   Ben likes to do <u>math</u> in the ___
5. A thick rug is a fat mat.
   A skinny needle is a ___ <u>pin</u>.
6. Mrs. Jay holds classes on the shore.
   She likes to ___ at the <u>beach</u>.

Write a Core Word from Lesson 21 that fits each group of words.

7. night, black, shadow, ___
8. pin, knife, ouch, ___
9. trees, swings, slides, ___

REVIEW

Write a Core Word from Lesson 22 that means the opposite of each word below.

10. boy
11. last
12. tall

Write a Core Word from Lesson 23 to fill the blank in each pair of sentences.

13. Sue: Did you eat all the carrots?
    Fred: Yes, I ate ___ one of them.
14. Lee: Is this my jacket?
    Lani: Yes, it is ___ jacket.
15. Carlos: Did you like the popcorn?
    Annie: Yes, it was ___ good!

25 Spelling Words with *br*, *fr*, and *tr*

FOCUS

CORE

1. train
2. brag
3. free
4. trade
5. frog
6. brick
7. frisky
8. bright
9. trick
10. broom

CHALLENGE

11. front
12. bread
13. tramp
14. friend
15. treat

Sound	Spelling
/br/	**br**ick
/fr/	**fr**og
/tr/	**tr**ade

Say each word. Listen for the first two sounds in *brick*, *frog*, and *trade*.

Study the spelling. How are the two beginning sounds spelled?

Write the words.

1–10. Write *br*, *fr*, and *tr* on the top of your paper. Write each of the ten Core Words under its beginning consonant blend.

11–15. Write the five Challenge Words. Ring the letters that spell the first two sounds.

SPELLING TIP
The /br/, /fr/, and /tr/ sounds are spelled *br*, *fr*, and *tr*.

Words and Meanings

Complete the story with Core Words.

My Pet and I

I have a new pet (1). I found it in a pond. So I got it for (2)!

I try not to (3) too much about my pet. It is a great frog. My frog has a (4) green color. It is also very smart and very (5). I plan to (6) my frog to do tricks. One (7) it has already learned is to jump through a hoop that I am holding.

My friend also has a pet frog. Sometimes we race our frogs on the red (8) path in front of my house. We use the handle of a (9) for the finish line.

Sometimes my frog wins.

Sometimes the other frog comes in first. Either way, I would not (10) my frog for another for anything. No, not ever!

11. railroad cars; to teach
12. shiny; smart

Many Meanings

Some words have more than one meaning. Write the Core Word that has both meanings.

13. no cost; to set loose
14. swap; job to make money
15. fool or cheat; a clever act

Join the Pieces
Write the five Core Words that are spelled by putting the bricks together. Be sure to use each brick part only one time.

1–5.

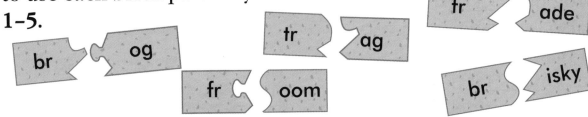

Spell the Words
Write the Core Words that fit the clues.

6–7. Two words that rhyme with *sick*.

8–9. Two words that have double vowels.

10. The word that ends with long *e* spelled *y*.

11. The word that rhymes with *fright*.

Put on Your Thinking Cap
Write the Core Word that finishes each sentence.

12. You scrub with a mop.
   You sweep with a ___.

13. A bus travels on a road.
   A ___ travels on a track.

14. A fish can swim.
   A ___ can hop.

15. Some houses are made out of wood.
   Some houses are made out of ___.

Do you have a pet? Would you like to have one? Follow the steps on pages 134–135 to write a story about a pet. Use three Core Words from this lesson.

Proofreding prakticee

1–3. Here is one student's story. Three words are spelled wrong. Write each word correctly.

> I have a new pet frog. It is brite green. I found it when I went fishing last week It is very friske. It would be fun to train it to do some trecks

4–5. Two periods were not put in at the ends of sentences. Copy the story. Correct all mistakes.

Now proofread your own story and correct any mistakes.

CORE		CHALLENGE
train	brick	front
brag	frisky	bread
free	bright	tramp
trade	trick	friend
frog	broom	treat

26 Spelling Words with *sl* and *sp*

CORE

1. slam
2. spin
3. speed
4. slip
5. space
6. slide
7. slick
8. speech
9. spy
10. sled

CHALLENGE

11. spoon
12. slant
13. speak
14. spark
15. spoke

FOCUS

Sound	Spelling
/sl/	**sl**ip
/sp/	**sp**in

Say each word. Listen for the first two sounds in *slip* and *spin*.

Study the spelling. How are the first two sounds spelled?

Write the words.

1–5. Write the five Core Words that begin with *sl*.

6–10. Write the five Core Words that begin with *sp*.

11–15. Write the five Challenge Words. Ring the letters that spell the two beginning sounds.

SPELLING TIP

The /sl/ and /sp/ sounds are spelled *sl* and *sp*.

WORDS and MEANINGS

Complete the story with Core Words.

Fun in the Winter

I love the winter. There is so much to do. When it snows, I pull my (1) to the top of a hill. Then I get on and (2) down. I pick up (3) going down. It feels as if I am flying through (4).

But I must watch where I am going. At the first sign of snow, our teacher gives the class a (5) on safety. We have to be careful so we do not (6) into a tree.

If there is no snow, I go ice skating. I like to skate on ice that is smooth and (7). Sometimes I (8) and fall. I hope no one is watching! Other times I (9) like a top! Then I hope my friends will (10) on me to see how well I skate!

Action Words

Slam and *spin* describe things you can do. Write the action word in each pair of words.

11. talk, book
12. van, drive
13. smile, story
14. apple, eat
15. sleep, cot
16. food, share

Word Play

Seek and Find

Write the five Core Words hidden in the Word Search. Be sure to look both across and down.

1–5.

c	a	s	p	i	n	t
d	e	l	o	s	p	y
s	l	i	d	e	k	m
r	s	p	e	e	c	h

Give a Speech

Write the missing Core Word in each title. Be sure you begin each word in the title with a capital letter.

6. How to ___ a Top
7. Two Ways to ___ Downhill with a Sled
8. Don't ___! You'll Get There.
9. My Life as a ___

Finish the Sign

Write the missing Core Word in each sign.

10.

Do not
_____
the door!

11.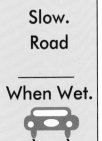

Slow.
Road
_____
When Wet.

12.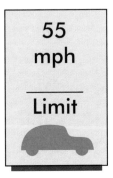

55
mph
_____
Limit

13.

For Sale:
Ice Skates
and
_____

14.

_____
Center
Next
Exit

Write a poem about something you like to do in the winter. Be sure to write a title for your poem. Use three Core Words from this lesson.

Prooofreding prakticee
a   c

1–3. Here is one student's poem. Three words are spelled wrong. Write each word correctly.

Ice Skating

I slep and slied,

I just cannot glide.

Please give me more spase,

So I do not fall on my face!

Proofread your own poem and correct any mistakes.

CORE		CHALLENGE
slam	slide	spoon
spin	slick	slant
speed	speech	speak
slip	spy	spark
space	sled	spoke

27 Spelling Words Ending with -s

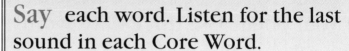

CORE

1. ducks
2. cows
3. whales
4. seals
5. rabbits
6. ants
7. chickens
8. zebras
9. snakes
10. animals

CHALLENGE

11. lions
12. bears
13. tigers
14. chipmunks
15. kangaroos

Say each word. Listen for the last sound in each Core Word.

Study the spelling. Does each Core Word mean one or more than one? Words that name more than one are called plurals. How is the last sound in each word spelled?

Write the words.

1–10. Write the ten Core Words. Ring the letter that shows *more than one.*

11–15. Write the five Challenge Words. Ring the letter that shows *more than one.*

SPELLING TIP

Add *-s* to most words to make them mean more than one.

WORDS and MEANINGS

Complete the story with Core Words.

A Trip to the Zoo

A zoo has all kinds of (1). In some zoos there are both farm animals and wild animals.

If you visit the farm animals, you will hear the clucking of (2). You can also hear the quacking of (3). You can watch (4) being milked. You can even feed clover to fluffy-tailed (5).

Bring a picnic lunch to the zoo with you. But be ready to share it with lots of black (6).

After lunch, you can visit the wild animals. You will see black and white (7) grazing in the grass. In the reptile house, there are lizards and (8).

At the zoo you will see harbor (9) diving for fish in a pool. But you will not see any blue (10). They are a little too big to fit in a pool!

WORD works

11. one highway, two ___
12. one pizza, four ___

More Plurals

Write a plural to finish each set of words.

13. one comb, several ___
14. one book, a shelf full of ___
15. one bird, a flock of ___

Name the Animals Write a Core Word for each clue.

1. They look like horses in funny clothes.
2. They slither close to the ground.
3. Smart ones are wise quackers.
4. They are at their best on a nest.
5. They are small but good workers.
6. They might want to be called bunnies.

Picture the Animals Write the Core Word that names each picture.

16. Write the Core Word that tells what all the living things in the pictures are called.

Write a report about an animal. Tell where it lives, what it eats, and how it looks. Follow the steps on pages 134–135. Use three Core Words from the lesson.

Proofreading practice

1–3. Here is part of one student's report. Three words are spelled wrong. Write each word correctly.

The biggest anmals in the world are wales. they live in the ocean just as seels do. They have flippers and fins. There are many kinds of whales. some eat fish.

4–5. Two capital letters were not put in at the beginnings of sentences. Copy the report. Correct all mistakes.

Proofread your own report and correct any mistakes.

CORE		CHALLENGE
ducks	ants	lions
cows	chickens	bears
whales	zebras	tigers
seals	snakes	chipmunks
rabbits	animals	kangaroos

Spelling Words That Sound Alike

FOCUS

CORE

1. see
2. sea
3. dear
4. deer
5. meet
6. meat
7. road
8. rode
9. dye
10. die

CHALLENGE

11. seam
12. seem
13. eye
14. too
15. to

Say each word. Listen for words that sound alike.

Study the spelling. How are the words spelled? Do some words have the same sounds but different spellings and meanings?

Write the words.

1–10. Write a Core Word. Then write the Core Word that sounds the same. Write all ten words.

11–15. Write the five Challenge Words. Ring the Challenge Word that is the long *i* sound.

SPELLING TIP
Some words have the same sounds but different spellings and meanings.

Complete the story with Core Words.

A BUS TRIP

Last summer I went to visit my (1) cousin. I (2) on the bus. I could (3) many things along the way. I saw a (4) running along the (5). Then it ran right in front of the bus. Luckily, we did not hit it. I am glad it did not get hurt and (6).

Later the bus stopped in view of the (7) so we could watch the sun go down. The sky turned a beautiful color. It looked as if it had been tinted with a red (8).

My cousin was at the station to (9) me. That night we cooked supper together. While we ate our (10) and potatoes, I told all about my bus trip.

Abbreviations

Rd. is an abbreviation for *Road.* Write each word and its abbreviation.

Mr. Ave. Dr. St. Nov.

11. Doctor
12. Mister
13. Street
14. Avenue
15. November

See the Difference Write the Core Word that fits each meaning.

1. look at
2. an ocean
3. you drive on it
4. went by bus

5. someone loved
6. an animal
7. something to eat
8. come together

9. stop living
10. used to color

Play with the Puzzle Write the pair of Core Words that fits in each puzzle. Be sure they rhyme with the word beside the puzzle.

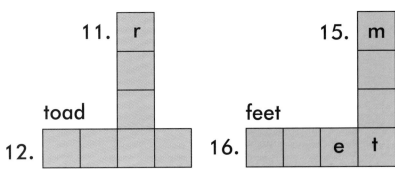

11. r
toad
12.

15. m
feet
16. e t

13.
here
14. d   r

bee 17.
18.   e
a

19.
fly
20.   y e

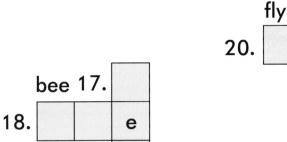

Where have you gone on a trip? How did you get there? Write a letter to a friend about your trip. Follow the steps on pages 134-135. Use four Core Words from the lesson.

Proofreding prakticee

1-4. Here is one student's letter. Four words are spelled wrong. Write each word correctly.

Dear Anita,

I went to visit with my deer friend Jess. I drove on a bumpy rode. I had a great time. It was a real treat to meat her family. I hope I will sea them again soon.

Your friend,

Marty

Now proofread your own letter and correct any mistakes.

CORE		CHALLENGE
see	meat	seam
sea	road	seem
dear	rode	eye
deer	dye	too
meet	die	to

29 Spelling Family Names

FOCUS

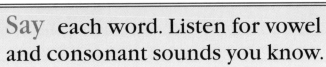

CORE

1. family
2. mother
3. sister
4. grandmother
5. aunt
6. baby
7. grandfather
8. uncle
9. father
10. brother

CHALLENGE

11. parent
12. children
13. together
14. person
15. twins

Say each word. Listen for vowel and consonant sounds you know.

Study the spelling. Look for spellings you know.

Write the words.

1–6. Write the six Core Words that end with *er*.

7–8. Write the two Core Words that end with long *e* spelled *y*.

9–10. Write *aunt* and *uncle*. Ring the vowels in each word.

11–15. Write the five Challenge Words. Ring the vowels.

SPELLING TIP

Some family names have spellings you know. Others have spellings that must be remembered.

WORDS and MEANINGS

Complete the story with Core Words.

All in the Family

I have a large (1). We like to get together for birthdays and holidays.

First there are my parents. Mom is the name I call my (2). I call my (3) Dad. He likes to pick flowers from his garden for our parties.

There are three other children in my family. We have a little (4) who is two months old. I also have a (5) named Jim and a (6) named Fay.

My mother's sister is my (7). My mother's mother is my (8). They always like to sing at our family parties.

My father's brother is my (9). My father's father is my (10). They like to help my father get the house ready for the parties.

it's A GIRL

WORD works

11. My mother will sing.
12. You and I can go.

Pronouns

Write each sentence using *He, She, They,* or *We* in place of the underlined words.

13. Our sister and brother ski.
14. His uncle works at home.
15. Her grandmother has a cat.

Map the Family
On a separate piece of paper, write the Core Words by filling in the missing letters on the family tree.

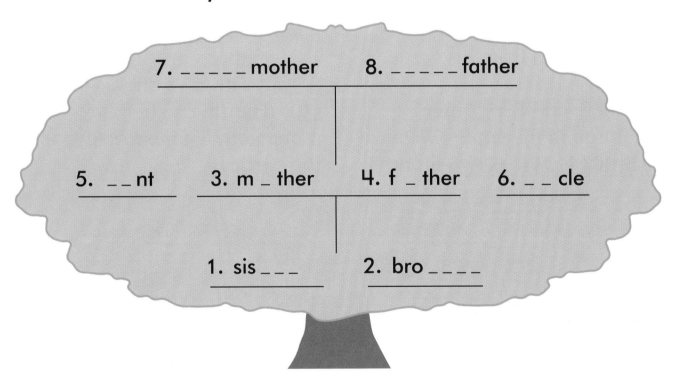

7. _ _ _ _ _ mother

8. _ _ _ _ _ father

5. _ _ nt

3. m _ ther

4. f _ ther

6. _ _ cle

1. sis _ _ _

2. bro _ _ _ _

Meet the Family
Write the Core Word that goes with each clue.

9. mom's sister

10. dad's brother

11. dad's mother

12. mom's father

13. boy child

14. girl child

15. all of the people

16. very young child

Write about a special person in your family. Follow the steps on pages 134–135 to tell about the person. Use three Core Words from this lesson.

Proofreding prakticee

1–4. Here is one student's description of a family member. Four words are spelled wrong. Write them correctly.

> Why is my ant so special. She is the one person in my famly who can do everything. She can fix a car. She is a great cook. She tells funny stories to my broter and sistre.

5. One question mark was not put in at the end of a question. Copy the description. Correct all mistakes.

Now proofread your own description and correct any mistakes.

CORE		CHALLENGE
family	baby	parent
mother	grandfather	children
sister	uncle	together
grandmother	father	person
aunt	brother	twins

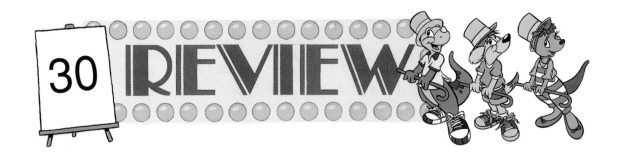

30 REVIEW

Write a Core Word from Lesson 25 that fits each group of words.

1. mop, sweep, dust, ___
2. snake, toad, pond, ___
3. airplane, bus, tracks, ___

Write a Core Word from Lesson 26 for each clue below.

4. something for riding on snow
5. turn around
6. to watch secretly

Write a Core Word from Lesson 27 to fit each picture clue. Each word means more than one.

7.

8.

9.

REVIEW

Write a Core Word from Lesson 28 to fill the blank in each pair of sentences.

10. Mike: Look at that red bird!
    Tina: I can't ___ it anywhere.
11. Carmen: That dress is an ugly color.
    Mama: Why don't we ___ it a new color?
12. Taylor: Why is Mom's car still here?
    Dad: She ___ her bike to work today.

Write the Core Word from Lesson 29 that goes with each word below as in the example.
grandmother – grandfather

13. mother – ___
14. sister – ___
15. aunt – ___

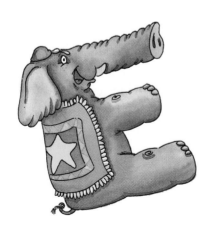

31 Spelling the /u̇/ Sound

FOCUS

CORE

1. put
2. hook
3. full
4. took
5. push
6. foot
7. book
8. pull
9. look
10. good

CHALLENGE

11. crook
12. stood
13. shook
14. wool
15. cookbook

Sound	Spelling
/u̇/	push hook

Say each word. Listen for the vowel sound you hear in *push* and *hook*. Note the sign for this sound.

Study the spelling. How is the vowel sound spelled in each word?

Write the words.

1–10. Write the ten Core Words. Ring the letters that spell the /u̇/ sound.

11–15. Write the five Challenge Words. Ring the letters that spell the /u̇/ sound.

SPELLING TIP

The vowel sound /u̇/ may be spelled *u* or *oo*.

Words and Meanings

Complete the story with Core Words.

Another Fish Story

I wanted to learn how to fish. So I went to the library to (1) for a (2). The shelves were (3) of all kinds of books. I soon found a guide to fishing that looked as if it would be (4). I (5) it out.

The author tells you everything you ever wanted to know about fishing. You even learn how to tie the (6) to the fishing line.

So I got into a rowboat for the first time. I did not even know where to (7) each (8). I started to (9) the oars toward me and then (10) them away. But the boat did not move. I guess I will have to read another book!

More Than One

Write the plurals of the underlined words below.

men   feet   children
mice   geese   women

11. one <u>foot</u>, two ___
12. one <u>man</u>, two ___
13. one <u>woman</u>, two ___

14. one <u>child</u>, two ___
15. one <u>mouse</u>, two ___
16. one <u>goose</u>, two ___

Word Play

Dial a Word Turn the letters on the dial to write four Core Words.

1-4.

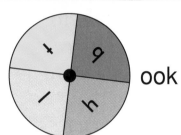

ook

Change the Meaning Write the Core Words that are the opposites of the underlined words.

5. The apple tasted <u>bad</u>.
6. Who <u>gave</u> these books?
7. My glass is <u>empty</u>.
8. Will you <u>push</u> the cart?

Write a Rhyme Write the Core Words that finish the rhymes.

9. "After I fix supper," said the cook.
   "I will read a good ___."

10. I sat for a while by the brook.
    Then I put some bait on my ___.

11. I know for sure that is the crook!
    I got a very close ___!

12. It is a shopping cart, not a rose bush.
    Please help me and give it a ___.

13. I need a place for my left foot.
    Where do you think it can be ___?

14. The chimney was full of soot.
    When I tried to clean it, it dropped on my ___.

Have you read any good books lately? Follow the steps on pages 134–135 to write a book report. Be sure to tell why you liked the book. Use three Core Words from this lesson.

Proofreding prakticee

1–3. Here is one student's book report. Three words are spelled wrong. Write each word correctly.

> Amelia Bedelia is a funny buk. Amelia is a gud cook, but she gets things mixed up. She poot bows on a chicken. She took some lightbulbs outside and hung them on a clothesline. I would like her as a friend!

Now proofread your own book report. Correct any mistakes.

CORE		CHALLENGE
put	foot	crook
hook	book	stood
full	pull	shook
took	look	wool
push	good	cookbook

32 Spelling Words Ending in -ed and -ing

CORE

1. mop
2. mopped
3. hit
4. hitting
5. bat
6. batting
7. tap
8. tapped
9. cut
10. cutting

CHALLENGE

11. running
12. skipping
13. digging
14. hopping
15. begged

Word	Ending	New Word
mop	*-ed*	mopped
hit	*-ing*	hitting

Say each word. Listen for the last sound you hear in *mop* and *hit.* Listen for the last sound you hear in *mopped* and *hitting.*

Study the spelling. What ending was added to *mop* and *hit?* Which letters were doubled when the ending was added?

Write the words.

  1–10. Write the ten Core Words. Ring the double consonants.

  11–15. Write the five Challenge Words. Ring the double consonants.

SPELLING TIP

Some words double the last consonant before adding the endings *-ed* and *-ing.*

WORDS and MEANINGS

Complete the story with Core Words.

Hometown Hero

Our baseball game was tied, five to five. "Who's up next?" I asked.

The coach (1) me on the shoulder. "You're next," she said. "Here's your (2)."

"Oh, no," I thought, as I (3) my forehead with my sleeve. "I am not very good at (4) the ball. I wish I had gone to more (5) practices. I should be home (6) the grass! Maybe I should tell the coach I have a (7) on my hand."

Instead, I walked slowly to home plate. I tried to give the first pitch a little (8), but I missed! Again, I had to (9) the sweat from my face. On the next pitch, I (10) a home run. The fans cheered! I was a hometown hero!

Adding -e

Add -e to change the vowel sounds. Write the new word.

tap + e = tape

11. can + e =   13. tub + e =   15. hop + e =

12. pin + e =   14. rob + e =   16. mad + e =

Connect the Ideas Write the missing Core Words.

1. *tennis* is to  as *baseball* is to ___

2. ⬛ is to *chop* as ✂ is to ___

3. *sweep* is to 🧹 as *scrub* is to ___

4. *clap* is to 👋 as ___ is to 👣

5. *kick* is to 🏈 as ___ is to *baseball*

Learn and Write Write the Core Words that fit the clues.

  6–8. Three Core Words with the same
        ending sound as *cat*.

 9–11. Three Core Words that end in **-ing.**

12–13. Two Core Words with the same ending
        sound as *top*.

14–15. Two Core Words that end in **-ed.**

16–18. Three Core Words with two syllables.

Use the Dictionary The different forms of a
word are usually listed after each entry in a
dictionary. Find the following Core Words in your
Speller Dictionary. Write the forms of the word
that are listed after the entry word.

19. bat   21. cut   23. tap

20. mop   22. hit   24. tooth

Have you ever gone to a ball game? Follow the steps on pages 134–135 to write a newspaper story about a game. Write a headline for your news story. Use three Core Words from this lesson.

Prooofreding prakticee

1–3. Here is a draft of one student's story. Three words are spelled wrong. Write each word correctly.

> **Last Game of the Season**
>
> The game was tied, five to five. Then the catcher for the Tigers came to bot. He het a home run. The Tigers were now in first place. I wished that I was at bat hiting the ball!

Proofread your own story. Correct any mistakes.

CORE		CHALLENGE
mop	batting	running
mopped	tap	skipping
hit	tapped	digging
hitting	cut	hopping
bat	cutting	begged

33 Spelling the /ou/ Sound

FOCUS

CORE

1. out
2. now
3. clown
4. our
5. down
6. sound
7. owl
8. house
9. town
10. loud

CHALLENGE

11. found
12. howl
13. south
14. crown
15. around

Sound	Spelling
/ou/	town sound

Say each word. Listen for the vowel sound in *town* and *sound*. Note the sign for this sound.

Study the spelling. How is the /ou/ sound spelled in each word?

Write the words.

1–10. Write the ten Core Words. Ring the letters that spell the /ou/ sound.

11–15. Write the five Challenge Words. Ring the letters that spell the /ou/ sound.

SPELLING TIP

The /ou/ sound may be spelled *ow* and *ou*.

WORDS and MEANINGS

Complete the story with Core Words.

COME TO THE CIRCUS

Listen everybody! The circus has come to (1). You do not have to leave your (2) to buy tickets for the show. Call right (3). Bring the whole family.

You will laugh at a funny (4) riding on a horse. You will see two people shot (5) of a cannon. Then they will come (6) in a net. Just remember to block your ears. The (7) of the cannon blast is very (8)! You will see (9) very own Skywalkers cross the high wire.

You can come to the circus during the day. Or, you can come in the evening if you are a night (10). Do not delay! Call today!

Words That Tell When

Now tells when something is happening. Write the word in each pair that tells *when*.

11. today, town

12. newspaper, never

13. always, apple

14. sometimes, sun

15. talk, tomorrow

16. yesterday, yawn

Look and Listen
Write the Core Words with the same ending sounds as the picture names.

1.

2.

3.

4.

5.

6.

7.

8–10.

Rhyme and Write
Finish the sentences with Core Words that rhyme with the underlined words.

11. The bounce of a ball is a <u>round</u> ___.
12. A person who is sad in the circus is a <u>frown</u> ___.
13. An animal on something you dry with is an ___ <u>towel</u>.
14. A little creature in your home is a ___ <u>mouse</u>.
15. A farm animal that is ready to give milk is a ___ <u>cow</u>.

Finish the News
Write the Core Words that finish the newspaper headlines. Be sure to begin the words with capital letters.

16.
THE CIRCUS IS COMING TO ___

17.
___ ROCKET BLASTS OFF!

18.
CAR RUNS ___ OF GAS ON HIGHWAY

WRITE ON YOUR OWN

Clowns like to make people laugh. Make a list of ways that you can make people laugh. Maybe you could tell a joke. Use three Core Words from this lesson.

Proofreding prakticee

1–3. Here is one student's list. Three words are spelled wrong. Write each word correctly.

Ways to Make People Laugh

1. Make a funny sownd.

2. Say up when you mean down.

3. Dress up like a cloun.

4. Hoot like an oul.

5. Draw a silly picture of your house.

Now proofread your own list. Correct any mistakes.

CORE		CHALLENGE
out	sound	found
now	owl	howl
clown	house	south
our	town	crown
down	loud	around

34 Spelling Compound Words

FOCUS

CORE

1. maybe
2. bedroom
3. lunchroom
4. into
5. something
6. nobody
7. doghouse
8. myself
9. inside
10. notebook

CHALLENGE

11. sailboat
12. downtown
13. weekend
14. everywhere
15. sandbox

Word + Word = Compound Word

dog + house =   doghouse

Say each word. Listen for the two words you hear in each Core Word.

Study the spelling. Look for familiar words in each word. How many words do you see in each Core Word?

Write the words.

1–10. Write the ten Core Words. Ring each of the two words that you find in the compound words.

11–15. Write the five Challenge Words. Ring each of the two words that you find in the compound words.

SPELLING TIP
Compound words are formed by joining two other words.

WORDS and MEANINGS

Complete the story with Core Words.

School Days

On school days I get up very early. There is (1) else up at this hour. I stay in my (2) and read for a while. Then I get dressed all by (3).

Before I leave, I always have (4) to eat. Sometimes I have toast, or (5) some cereal. While I eat, I hear scratching on the door. It is my dog. He sleeps in a (6) in our yard at night. I open the door and let him (7).

When it is time to leave, I get my things together. I check to make sure I have my pencil and (8). Most days I put my lunch (9) my backpack. Sometimes I like to buy lunch at school. Everyone in my class eats in the (10). At the door, I pat my dog and off I go!

Words That Tell Where

Inside tells where something happened. Write the word in each pair that tells *where.*

11. out, every   13. full, down   15. smart, around
12. with, below   14. upstairs, something   16. across, first

Put the Pieces Together Write the Core

Words that are spelled by fitting the pieces of the
puzzles together.

1-5.

may   self   some   side   in

book   my   thing   note   be

Join the Words Write the Core Words that are
made by joining two words in each sentence into a
compound word.

6. I will eat my lunch in my room today.
7. Did you find a note in your spelling book?
8. You may fall on the steps, so please be careful.
9. My dog likes to stay in the house at night.
10. Make the bed in your room before you leave.
11. There are no bones in the body of a worm.
12. Take the box in the kitchen to the shed.

Think of the first day of school this year. How did you feel? What did you do? Follow the steps on pages 134–135 to tell about that day. Use three Core Words from this lesson.

Proofreading practice

1–3. Here is one student's description. Three words are spelled wrong. Write each word correctly.

> I walked to school by miself. It rained all day so we stayed inside for recess We ate in the new lunchrum Our teacher gave us a spelling notbook. I made a new friend. I was busy so the day passed by very quickly.

4–5. Two periods were not put in at the ends of sentences. Copy the description. Correct all mistakes.

Proofread your own description. Correct any mistakes.

CORE		CHALLENGE
maybe	nobody	sailboat
bedroom	doghouse	downtown
lunchroom	myself	weekend
into	inside	everywhere
something	notebook	sandbox

35 Spelling Number Words

CORE

1. one
2. two
3. three
4. four
5. five
6. six
7. seven
8. eight
9. nine
10. ten

CHALLENGE

11. count
12. add
13. numbers
14. minus
15. second

Say each word. Listen for familiar vowel and consonant sounds.

Study the spelling. Do you see some short and long vowel spellings you have studied? Do you see any unusual spellings?

Write the words.

1–10. Write the ten Core Words. Ring the short and long vowel spellings you see.

11–15. Write the five Challenge Words. Ring any vowel spellings you know.

SPELLING TIP
Some number words have common spellings. Others must be remembered.

WORDS and MEANINGS

Complete the story with Core Words.

Just the Numbers, Please

Ten students in the class were divided into two teams. Five children were on each team.

Here are the ten math problems they had to solve:

Two plus five is (1).

Three plus five is (2).

Six take away four is (3).

Seven take away six is (4).

Four plus six is (5).

Nine take away four is (6).

Three plus one is (7).

Eight take away five is (8).

Two plus four is (9).

Six plus three is (10).

Each student had to give the answer to one problem. How many would you have gotten right? Would you have helped your team to win?

MATH TEST
23   54
+10   -43

Homophones

Some number words are homophones. Write each sentence using the correct spelling and meaning.

11. I go ___ school. (to, two)
12. Here is ___ hat. (one, won)

13. We ___ lunch. (eight, ate)
14. Pass ___ cups. (for, four)

Look and Count

Write the Core Word that tells how many of each thing listed below you find in the picture.

1. ___ balls
2. ___ clocks
3. ___ pictures
4. ___ shoes
5. ___ fish
6. ___ books

Tell How Many

Write the Core Words that answer the questions.

7. How many fingers are on one hand?
8. How many toes are on both feet?
9. How many ears does a dog have?
10. How many sides are in a △ ?
11. How many noses are on one face?
12. How many people are in two pairs of twins?
13. How many days are in one week?
14. How many letters are in the word *classroom?*
15. What is six plus two?

WRITE ON YOUR OWN

THE REMAINDERS

How old are you? How many people are in your family? Follow the steps on pages 134–135 to write a story about yourself. Use three Core Words from this lesson.

Proofreding prakticee
a   c

1–3. Here is one student's story. Three words are spelled wrong. Write each word correctly.

I am sevin years old. I am in the second grade. There are for children in my family. I have won brother and two sisters. I also have three pet goldfish. When I am eight years old, I will get a new pet. I hope it is a dog.

Now proofread your own story. Correct any mistakes.

CORE		CHALLENGE
one	six	count
two	seven	add
three	eight	numbers
four	nine	minus
five	ten	second

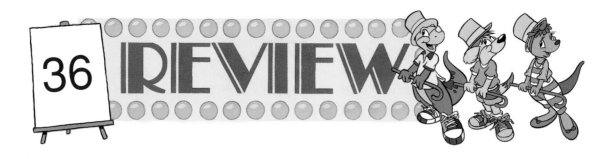

Write a Core Word from Lesson 31 to finish each sentence. The missing word will rhyme with the underlined word.

1. A nice log is ___ wood.
2. To press on a little tree is to ___ a bush.
3. At the library you look for a ___.

Write a Core Word from Lesson 32 to fill the space. The word you write will add **-ed** or **-ing** to the underlined word.

4. I will bat for Jay. Sam is ___ for Julie.
5. Next week Fred will mop the floor. Yesterday Ed ___ it.
6. Tap carefully on the door. Last year it was ___ too hard.

Write the Core Word from Lesson 33 that means the same as each underlined part of the poems below.

7. "This is the home that Jack built."
   —NURSERY RHYME

8. "Jack fell from a higher to a lower place and broke his crown."
   —NURSERY RHYME

9. "The bird with large staring eyes and the Pussy-Cat went to sea."
   —EDWARD LEAR

REVIEW

Write a Core Word from Lesson 34 for each clue below.

10. It is where you eat at school.
11. You write things in it.
12. You say this instead of *yes* or *no*.

Write a Core Word from Lesson 35 to answer each question using the pictures.

13. How many teeth?

14. How many legs?

15. How many sides?

Steps in the Writing Process

Here are some steps you might want to use to help you write.

1 Prewriting

Think about what you want to write about.

What have you done or seen?
What things do you remember?
Ask a friend for ideas.

Explore your topic.

Make a list of things that pop into your head.
Draw a picture of your idea.
Share your idea with others.

2 Drafting

Make a first try at writing.

Write quickly to get your ideas down.
Do not worry about mistakes now.

134

3 Revising

Carefully read what you have written.

Change your words, sentences, or ideas to make
them better.

Read your writing to someone else.
Ask how to make it better.

4 Proofreading

Read what you have written again.

Did you spell all words correctly? Did you use capitals,
periods, and question marks correctly?

5 Publishing

Make a neat copy of your paper.
Be careful not to make new mistakes.

Add pictures, a title, or other special things.

Share your writing with others.

How to Use the Dictionary

The word you look up in a dictionary is called an **entry word.** The entry words in a dictionary are given in ABC order. A dictionary tells you how to say the word. It also tells you what the word means. Some words have more than one meaning. When they do, the dictionary gives you each meaning.

Study the dictionary entries below. Notice how much you can learn about a word from a dictionary.

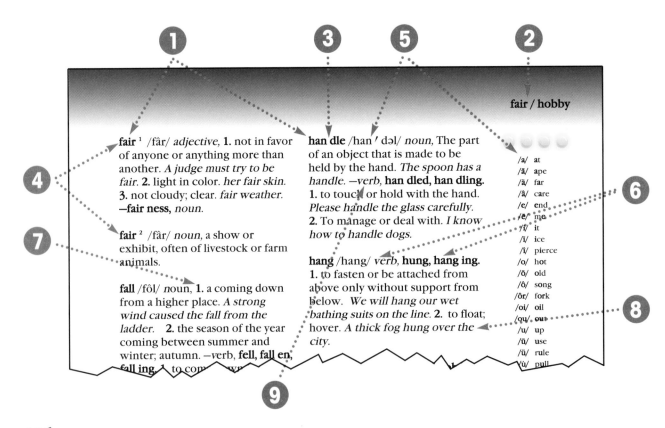

fair[1] /fâr/ *adjective,* **1.** not in favor of anyone or anything more than another. *A judge must try to be fair.* **2.** light in color. *her fair skin.* **3.** not cloudy; clear. *fair weather.* —**fair ness,** *noun.*

fair[2] /fâr/ *noun,* a show or exhibit, often of livestock or farm animals.

fall /fôl/ *noun,* **1.** a coming down from a higher place. *A strong wind caused the fall from the ladder.* **2.** the season of the year coming between summer and winter; autumn. —*verb,* **fell, fall en, fall ing.** to com

han dle /han′ dəl/ *noun,* The part of an object that is made to be held by the hand. *The spoon has a handle.* —*verb,* **han dled, han dling. 1.** to touch or hold with the hand. *Please handle the glass carefully.* **2.** To manage or deal with. *I know how to handle dogs.*

hang /hang/ *verb,* **hung, hang ing. 1.** to fasten or be attached from above only without support from below. *We will hang our wet bathing suits on the line.* **2.** to float; hover. *A thick fog hung over the city.*

fair / hobby

/a/ at
/ā/ ape
/ä/ far
/â/ care
/e/ end
/ē/ me
/i/ it
/ī/ ice
/î/ pierce
/o/ hot
/ō/ old
/ô/ song
/ôr/ fork
/oi/ oil
/ou/ out
/u/ up
/ū/ use
/ü/ rule
/u̇/ pull

136

1. The **entry word** is the word you look up. Entry words are in dark type and listed in ABC order.

2. At the top of each dictionary page are two words called **guide words.** They are the first and last entry words appearing on that page. Guide words help you find an entry word quickly.

3. Words with more than one **syllable** are shown in two parts. A space separates the syllables.

4. Sometimes there is more than one entry for a word. When this happens, each entry is numbered.

5. After the entry word is the **pronunciation.** It is given between two lines. This shows how to say the word. A key shows the sound for each letter in the respelling. The key is found on each page of the dictionary.

6. The **part of speech** and other forms of the entry word are given after the pronunciation.

7. One or more **definitions** are given for each entry word. If there is more than one definition, the definitions are numbered.

8. Sometimes the entry word is used in a **sample sentence** to help explain the meaning.

9. Some words can be more than one part of speech. If so, the dictionary sometimes gives another definition for the entry word.

Speller Dictionary

··· **A** ·············

add /ad/ *verb* **add ed, add ing. 1.** to find the sum of two or more numbers. *If you add 2 and 7, you will get 9.* **2.** to put in or on as something extra. *We added a porch to our house.*

a larm /ə lärm′/ *noun, plural* **a larms.** a bell, buzzer, or other device used to wake people up or to warn them of danger. *Set the alarm for seven o'clock.*

and /ənd, ən/ *conjunction* in addition to. *The girls and boys will read.*

an i mal /an′ ə məl/ *noun, plural* **an i mals. 1.** a living thing that takes in food and moves about and that is made up of many cells. Unlike plants, animals do not have to stay in one place, and they cannot make their own food. Jellyfish, worms, clams, insects, birds, fish, mammals, and human beings are all animals. **2.** animals other than humans. *My aunt and uncle raise animals on their farm.*

ant /ant/ *noun, plural* **ants.** a small insect related to bees and wasps. Ants live together in large groups called colonies.

an y /en′ ē/ *adjective* one or some. *Sit in any chair.* — *adverb* to any extent or degree. *Are you feeling any better?* — *pronoun* any one or ones. *Any of these books is sure to interest you.*

arm /ärm/ *noun, plural* **arms.**
1. the part of the body between the shoulder and the wrist. *He broke his arm.*
2. anything shaped like an arm. *The arm of the green chair is loose.*

a round /ə round'/ *adverb*
1. in a circle. *The wheel spun around.* **2.** somewhere near. *Why not stay around for a few minutes.*
—*preposition* in a circle or path that surrounds. *I wore a belt around my waist.*

art /ärt/ *noun, plural* **arts.**
1. an activity by which one creates a work of beauty or special meaning. Painting, sculpture, composing, and writing are forms of art. Murals, ballets, and poems are works of art.

as /az/ *adverb* **1.** to the same degree or extent that. *They were proud as they could be.*
2. in the same way or manner that. *Pronounce the word as I am pronouncing it.*
—*preposition* in the manner, role, or function of. *I'm speaking to you as a friend.*

ask /ask/ *verb* **asked, ask ing.** to inquire. *We asked how to get to town.*

aunt /ant, änt/ *noun, plural* **aunts. 1.** the sister of one's mother or father. *The lady is one of my aunts.* **2.** the wife of one's uncle.

a way /ə wā'/ *adjective*
1. distance. *The town is 3 miles away.* **2.** absent; gone. *My cousin has gone away.* —*adverb* **1.** from this or that place. *The frightened rabbit hopped away.* **2.** at a distance. *They stood far away from us.*

ba by /bā' bē/ *noun, plural* **ba bies. 1.** a very young child; infant. *The baby is learning how to walk.* **2.** the youngest person in a family or group. *I am the baby of the family.*

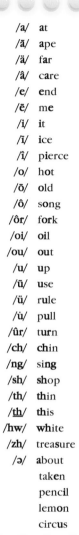

/a/	at
/ā/	ape
/ä/	far
/â/	care
/e/	end
/ē/	me
/i/	it
/ī/	ice
/î/	pierce
/o/	hot
/ō/	old
/ô/	song
/ôr/	fork
/oi/	oil
/ou/	out
/u/	up
/ū/	use
/ü/	rule
/ù/	pull
/ûr/	turn
/ch/	chin
/ng/	sing
/sh/	shop
/th/	thin
/th/	this
/hw/	white
/zh/	treasure
/ə/	about
	taken
	pencil
	lemon
	circus

backpack /bak′ pak′ / *noun, plural* **back packs.** a bag that is used to carry things on the back. It has straps for the shoulders and sometimes has a metal frame.

bad /bad/ *adjective* **worse, worst. 1.** having little quality or worth. *How can anyone watch such a bad television program?* **2.** not well or happy, especially because of regret or sadness. *I felt bad when our team lost the game.*

bait /bāt/ *noun, plural* **baits.** food put on a hook or in a trap to attract and catch fish or other animals. *We use worms for bait.*

bal loon /bə lün′/ *noun, plural* **bal loons.** a rubber or plastic bag filled with air or gas. Small balloons are used as children's toys or for decoration. Large balloons are filled with hot air or some other very light gas so that they rise and float. These balloons have cabins or baskets for carrying

passengers or scientific instruments.

band /band/ *noun, plural* **bands.** a group of musicians playing together. *The band played at the game.*

barn /bärn/ *noun, plural* **barns.** a building on a farm that is used to store hay and grain, and to house cows and horses. *The cows stay in the barn when it is cold.*

bat [1] /bat/ *noun, plural* **bats.** a strong wooden stick or club. A bat is used to hit the ball in baseball and softball. —*verb* **bat ted, bat ting.** to use a bat in baseball and other games. *Our team is batting next.*

bat [2] /bat/ *noun, plural* **bats.** a small furry animal that flies. *There are bats in the barn.*

bath /bath/ *noun, plural* **baths** /ba<u>th</u>z, baths/. **1.** a washing of something in water. *Let's give the dog a bath.* **2.** the water used for bathing. *The bath was too hot.*

bear /bâr/ *noun, plural* **bears.** a large, heavy animal with thick shaggy fur. A bear has sharp claws and a very short tail. There are many kinds of bears, including the black bear, brown bear, grizzly bear, and the polar bear.

bed room /bed′ rüm′, bed′ rùm′/ *noun, plural* **bed rooms.** a room for sleeping.

beg /beg/ *verb* **begged, beg ging. 1.** to ask in a humble way. *The late guest begged to be excused.* **2.** to ask in an eager or insisting way; plead. *The child begged to go to the rodeo.*

bend /bend/ *verb* **bent, bend ing.** to change the shape of something by making it curved. *We will bend the wire.*

bird /bûrd/ *noun, plural* **birds.** an animal that has wings, two legs, and a body covered with feathers. *Most birds can fly.*

blank /blangk/ *noun, plural* **blanks.** an empty space to be filled in. *Fill in the blank with your name.*

blan ket /blang′ kit/ *noun, plural* **blan kets.** a covering to use to keep warm while sleeping. *We used a warm blanket on our bed.*

blast /blast/ *verb* **blast ed, blast ing.** to take off in flight propelled by a rocket. *We saw the spacecraft blast off.*

blaze /blāz/ *noun, plural* **blaz es. 1.** a bright flame. *We could see the blaze of the burning building.* **2.** a bright light. *We shielded our eyes from the blaze of the sun.*

blend /blend/ *noun, plural* **blends.** a mixture. *This drink is a blend of fruit juices.*

blimp /blimp/ *noun, plural* **blimps.** an airship that does not have a rigid shape. *A blimp was in the sky near my house.*

/a/ at
/ā/ ape
/ä/ far
/â/ care
/e/ end
/ē/ me
/i/ it
/ī/ ice
/î/ pierce
/o/ hot
/ō/ old
/ô/ song
/ôr/ fork
/oi/ oil
/ou/ out
/u/ up
/ū/ use
/ü/ rule
/ù/ pull
/ûr/ turn
/ch/ chin
/ng/ sing
/sh/ shop
/th/ thin
/th/ this
/hw/ white
/zh/ treasure
/ə/ about
taken
pencil
lemon
circus

blink /blingk/ *verb* **blinked, blink ing.** to close and open the eyes quickly. *Everyone blinked when they walked out of the dark into the light.*

block /blok/ *noun, plural* **blocks.** a piece of something hard and solid, with flat surfaces. *The house was built of blocks of rock.*

blow [1] /blō/ *noun, plural* **blows.** a hard hit or stroke. A blow may be made with the fist, a tool, or some other object. *A heavy blow with a hammer drove the nail into the board.*

blow [2] /blō/ *verb* **blew, blown, blow ing. 1.** to move with speed or force. *An autumn breeze blew the leaves across the yard.* **2.** to send out a strong current of air. *Blow on your hands to warm them.*

boat /bōt/ *noun, plural* **boats. 1.** a small vessel that is used for traveling on water. A boat is moved by using oars, paddles, sails, or a motor. Passengers in boats usually sit in the open air. **2.** a ship. An ocean liner is a boat.

book /bùk/ *noun, plural* **books. 1.** sheets of paper fastened together between two covers. The pages of a book usually have writing or printing on them. *I like the pictures in these books.*

boot /bùt/ *noun, plural* **boots.** a covering for the foot and lower part of the leg. Boots are usually made of leather or rubber.

both /bōth/ *adjective* one and also the other; the two. *Both players are left-handed.* —*pronoun* the one and also the other. *You may need a pencil and paper, so bring both.*

brag /brag/ *verb* **bragged, brag ging.** to speak with too much praise about what one does or owns; boast. *Stop bragging about how smart you are.*

bread /bred/ *noun, plural* **breads.** a food made by mixing flour or meal with water or milk, and then baking it in the oven. *We eat different types of bread.*

brick /brik/ *noun, plural* **bricks.** a block of clay baked in a kiln or in the sun. *Bricks are used in building.*

bright /brīt/ *adjective* **bright er, bright est.** **1.** giving much light. *The bright light of the sun hurt the swimmer's eyes.* **2.** clear, strong. *Let's paint the chair a brighter color.*

bring /bring/ *verb* **brought, bring ing. 1.** to cause something or someone to come with you. *Remember to bring your book home.* **2.** to cause something to come or happen. *The heavy rains will bring floods.*

broom /brüm, brum/ *noun, plural* **brooms.** a brush with a long handle, used for sweeping. *We used the broom to sweep up the dirt.*

broth er /bru<u>th</u>′ ər/ *noun, plural* **broth ers.** a boy or man having the same parents as another person. *The small one is one of my brothers.*

bunch /bunch/ *noun, plural* **bunch es.** a number of things fastened together. *That is a big bunch of grapes.*

came /kām/ *verb* past tense of *come.* See **come.**

camp /kamp/ *noun, plural* **camps.** an outdoor place with tents where people sleep for a time. *The camp is near a river.*

cane /kān/ *noun, plural* **canes. 1.** a stick used to help someone walk. *I need a cane to walk.* **2.** the long, woody, joined stem of bamboo. *Bamboo is a cane.*

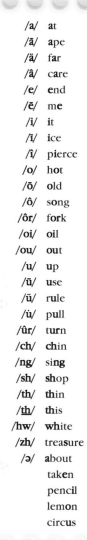

/a/	at
/ā/	ape
/ä/	far
/â/	care
/e/	end
/ē/	me
/i/	it
/ī/	ice
/î/	pierce
/o/	hot
/ō/	old
/ô/	song
/ôr/	fork
/oi/	oil
/ou/	out
/u/	up
/ū/	use
/ü/	rule
/ù/	pull
/ûr/	turn
/ch/	chin
/ng/	sing
/sh/	shop
/th/	thin
/<u>th</u>/	this
/hw/	white
/zh/	treasure
/ə/	about
	taken
	pencil
	lemon
	circus

cart /kärt/ *noun, plural* **carts.** a strong wagon with two wheels that is used to carry a load. Carts are usually pulled by horses, mules, or oxen.

cash /kash/ *noun* money in the form of coins and paper bills. *Instead of paying for the coat with a check, I paid for it with cash.* —*verb* **cashed, cash ing.** to get or give cash for. *We have to stop at the bank and cash a check.*

cast /kast/ *verb* **cast, cast ing.** the act of throwing. *We cast our fishing lines into the river.*

chick en /chik′ ən/ *noun, plural* **chick ens.** a bird that is raised on farms for its meat and eggs. Chickens may be of many different colors.

child /chīld/ *noun, plural* **chil dren.** a son or daughter. *The parents were very proud of their only child.*

chil dren /chil′ drən/ *plural noun* plural of *child. Three*

children stood at the bus stop.

chip munk /chip′ mungk/ *noun, plural* **chip munks.** a small animal that has brown fur with dark stripes on its back and tail. Chipmunks are rodents and are related to squirrels.

choke /chōk/ *verb* **choked, chok ing.** to stop or hold back the breathing of by squeezing or blocking the windpipe. *That tight collar could choke the dog.*

chore /chôr/ *noun, plural* **chores. 1.** a small job or task. *Feeding the cat is my chore.* **2.** a hard or unpleasant task.

clash /klash/ *noun, plural* **clash es.** a loud harsh sound like pieces of metal striking against each other. *The band ended the parade music with a clash of cymbals.*

click /klik/ *noun, plural* **clicks.** a light sharp sound. *We heard the click of a key in the lock.*

clock /klok/ *noun, plural* **clocks.** a device showing time. *The clock shows it is six o'clock.*

clown /kloun/ *noun, plural* **clowns.** a person who makes people laugh by playing tricks or doing stunts. A clown in a circus often wears funny clothing and makeup. *Clowns are funny.*

coach /kōch/ *noun, plural* **coach es. 1.** a large, closed carriage pulled by horses. A coach has seats inside for passengers and a raised seat outside for the driver. **2.** a teacher or trainer of athletes. *The basketball coach made the team practice extra hours this week.*

coat /kōt/ *noun, plural* **coats. 1.** a piece of outer clothing with sleeves. *I have a new winter coat.* **2.** the outer covering of an animal. *Our dog has a shaggy brown coat.* **3.** layer. *The painters put on a new coat of paint on our house.*

come /kum/ *verb* **came, come, com ing.** to move forward. *Does your dog come to you when you call it?*

cook book /kùk′ bùk′/ *noun, plural* **cook books.** a book of recipes and other information about food. *I looked in a cookbook to find out how to roast a turkey.*

cot /kot/ *noun, plural* **cots.** a narrow bed. Cots usually have a frame that can be folded and put away.

count /kount/ *verb* **count ed, count ing.** to find out how many of something there are; add up. *Count the number of books on the shelf.*

cow /kou/ *noun, plural* **cows. 1.** the fully grown female of cattle. Cows are raised for their milk, meat, and hide. **2.** the female of some other large mammals. A female moose, elephant, or whale is called a cow.

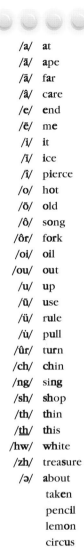

/a/	at
/ā/	ape
/ä/	far
/â/	care
/e/	end
/ē/	me
/i/	it
/ī/	ice
/î/	pierce
/o/	hot
/ō/	old
/ô/	song
/ôr/	fork
/oi/	oil
/ou/	out
/u/	up
/ū/	use
/ü/	rule
/ù/	pull
/ûr/	turn
/ch/	chin
/ng/	sing
/sh/	shop
/th/	thin
/th/	this
/hw/	white
/zh/	treasure
/ə/	about
	taken
	pencil
	lemon
	circus

cream /krēm/ *noun, plural* **creams.** the yellowish white part of milk. *Butter is made from cream.*

crook /krùk/ *noun, plural* **crooks. 1.** a bent part; curve. *I carry my umbrella in the crook of my arm.* **2.** a shepherd's staff with a hook at the top. **3.** a person who is not honest.

cross /krôs/ *adjective* **cross er, cross est.** in a bad temper; grouchy. *People sometimes get cross when you point out their mistakes.*

crown /kroun/ *noun, plural* **crowns.** a covering for the head worn by kings and queens. A crown is often made of silver set with jewels. *The king has two crowns.*

cry /krī/ *verb* **cried, cry ing. 1.** to shed tears; weep. *The hungry baby cried.* **2.** to call out loudly; shout. *The people in the burning building were crying for help.*

cut /cut/ *verb* **cut, cut ting. 1.** to divide, pierce, open, or take away a part with something sharp. *We could not untie the knot so we had to cut the string.* **2.** to make by using a sharp tool. *We cut a hole in the door so the cat could come in and go out.*

cute /kūt/ *adjective* **cut er, cut est.** delightful or pretty. *This is the cutest puppy I've ever seen.*

dark /därk/ *noun* having little or no light. *The night was dark because the clouds were covering the moon.*

dash /dash/ *verb,* **dashed, dash ing. 1.** to move fast; rush. *We dashed to the waiting bus.* **2.** to destroy or ruin. *Spraining my ankle dashed my hopes of running in the race.* —*noun, plural* **dash es. 1.** a fast movement or sudden rush. *When the rain began we made a dash for cover.* **2.** a small amount that is added or mixed in. *Add a dash of salt to the soup.*

dear /dîr/ *adjective* **dear er, dear est.** much loved. *This is my dearest friend.* —*noun, plural* **dears.** a much loved person. *You are a dear to come over and help.*

deep /dēp/ *adjective* **1.** far from the surface. *I don't swim in the deep end of the swimming pool.* **2.** great in degree; extreme. *The weary child fell into a deep sleep.*

deer /dîr/ *noun, plural* **deer.** an animal that has hooves, chews its cud, and runs very fast. A male deer has antlers that are shed every year and grow back the next year.

desk /desk/ *noun, plural* **desks.** a piece of furniture used for reading or writing. *There are four drawers in my desk.*

die /dī/ *verb* **died, dy ing.** to stop living; become dead.

The flowers died during the dry spell.

dig /dig/ *verb* **dig ging, dug. 1.** to break up or turn over the earth with a shovel, the hands, or claws. *Our dog likes to dig in the yard for bones.* **2.** to make or get by digging. *The settlers had to dig a well for water.*

din o saur /dī′ nə sôr′/ *noun, plural* **din o saurs.** one of a large group of extinct reptiles that lived millions of years ago. Some dinosaurs were the largest land animals that have ever lived, and others were small as cats.

dirt /dûrt/ *noun* mud, dust, or other material that makes something unclean. *The children washed the dirt off their hands before coming to dinner.*

dish /dish/ *noun, plural* **dish es** a plate or shallow bowl used for holding food. *We set the table with our good china dishes.*

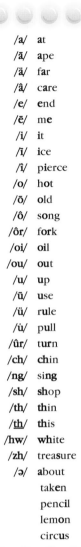

/a/	at
/ā/	ape
/ä/	far
/â/	care
/e/	end
/ē/	me
/i/	it
/ī/	ice
/î/	pierce
/o/	hot
/ō/	old
/ô/	song
/ôr/	fork
/oi/	oil
/ou/	out
/u/	up
/ū/	use
/ü/	rule
/ů/	pull
/ûr/	turn
/ch/	chin
/ng/	sing
/sh/	shop
/th/	thin
/th/	this
/hw/	white
/zh/	treasure
/ə/	about
	taken
	pencil
	lemon
	circus

dock /dock/ *noun, plural* **docks.** a platform where boats or ships are tied up. *We pulled the boat to the dock.*

does /duz/ *verb* a form of the present tense of *do* that is used with she, he, it, or the name of a person, place, or thing. *The artist does beautiful paintings.*

dog /dôg/ *noun, plural* **dogs.** an animal that has four legs and makes a barking noise. Dogs have claws and sharp teeth for eating meat. Dogs are related to coyotes, wolves, and foxes.

dog house /dôg′ hous′/ *noun, plural* **dog hous es.** a shelter built for a dog.

down[1] /doun/ *adverb* from a higher to a lower place. *The painter climbed down from the ladder.*

down[2] /doun/ *noun* fine, soft feathers. *Baby birds have down until their regular feathers grow in.*

down town /doun′ toun′/ *adverb* to or in the main part or business district of a town. *We went downtown to see a movie.* — *adjective* going to or located in the main part of town. *The downtown stores are larger than stores in our neighborhood.*

dream /drēm/ *noun, plural* **dreams.** a series of thoughts, feelings, and apparent sights that a person has while asleep. *I had a dream that I was flying.*

dress /dres/ *noun, plural* **dress es.** a garment worn by a girl or a woman. *Joan has a new dress.*

drip /drip/ *verb* **dripped, drip ping.** to fall in drops. *Be careful not to drip paint on the rug.*

drive /drīv/ *verb* **drove, driv en, driv ing.** to operate and steer a car. *My teacher taught me to drive a car.*

drove /drōv/ *verb* past tense of *drive.* See **drive.**

drum /drum/ *noun, plural* **drums.** a musical instrument that is hollow and covered at the top and bottom with a material that is stretched tight. *My brother plays the drum at school.*

dry /drī/ *adjective* **dri er, dri est.** not wet or damp. *Cactuses grow well in a dry climate.*

duck /duk/ *noun, plural* **ducks.** a water bird that has a broad bill and webbed feet that help it to swim. There are both wild and tame ducks.

dump /dump/ *verb* **dumped, dump ing.** to drop, unload, or empty. *I dumped my books on the table.*

dust /dust/ *noun* tiny pieces of earth, dirt, or other matter. *The horse kicked up a cloud of dust.*

dye /dī/ *noun, plural* **dyes.** a substance that is used to give a particular color to hair, food, cloth or other materials. —*verb* **dyed, dye ing.** to color or stain something. *When the blue curtains faded, we dyed them red.*

each /ēch/ *adjective* every one of two or more things or persons thought of as individuals or one at a time. *Each player gets a turn.*

egg /eg/ *noun, plural* **eggs.** a round or oval body with a shell produced by chickens, birds, and other female animals. *I eat an egg once a week.*

eight /āt/ *noun, plural* **eights.** one more than seven; 8. *Will eight hotdogs be enough?*

eve ry /ev′ rē/ *adjective* each person or thing of all the people or things that are part of a group. *Every student in the class is here today.*

/a/	at
/ā/	ape
/ä/	far
/â/	care
/e/	end
/ē/	me
/i/	it
/ī/	ice
/î/	pierce
/o/	hot
/ō/	old
/ô/	song
/ôr/	fork
/oi/	oil
/ou/	out
/u/	up
/ū/	use
/ü/	rule
/ù/	pull
/ûr/	turn
/ch/	chin
/ng/	sing
/sh/	shop
/th/	thin
/th/	this
/hw/	white
/zh/	treasure
/ə/	about
	taken
	pencil
	lemon
	circus

149

eve ry where /ev′ rē hwâr, ev′ rē wâr′/ *adverb* in every place; in all places. *Have you looked everywhere for the book?*

eye /ī/ *noun, plural* **eyes.** one of the organs of the body by which humans and other animals see or sense light. *I have brown eyes.*

fam i ly /fam′ ə lē, fam′ lē/ *noun, plural* **fam i lies.** a group of people who are related. *The average family has three or four members.*

farm /färm/ *noun, plural* **farms.** a piece of land that is used to raise crops and animals. *The farm is near the small town.*

fast /fast/ *adverb* **fast er, fast est.** moving quickly. *A fast train rushed by.*

fat /fat/ *adjective* **1.** having much fat or flesh on the body. **2.** having much in it.

All that money makes your wallet fat.

fa ther /fä′ <u>th</u>ər/ *noun, plural* **fa thers. 1.** a male parent. **2.** priest. *My father is good to me.*

fed /fed/ *verb* past tense of feed. See **feed.**

feed /fēd/ *verb* **fed, feed ing.** to give food to. *May I feed the baby?*

fight /fīt/ *noun, plural* **fights.** a struggle between animals, persons, or groups who use weapons or their bodies against each other. In a fight, each side tries to hurt the other or to protect itself against the other. *Two dogs had a fight over the bone.*

find /fīnd/ *verb* **found, find ing. 1.** to discover or come upon by accident. *I found a wallet on the sidewalk.* **2.** to get or learn by thinking or calculating. *Please find the sum of this column of numbers.*

first /fûrst/ *adjective* before all others. *George Washington was the first president of the United States.* —*adverb* before all others. *She was ranked first in her class.*

fish /fish/ *noun, plural* **fish, fish es. 1.** a cold-blooded animal that lives in water. Fish have backbones, gills for breathing, and, usually, fins and scales. **2.** the flesh of fish used as food. —*verb* **fished, fish ing. 1.** to catch or try to catch fish. **2.** to search by groping. *I fished around in my pocket for the key.*

five /fīv/ *noun, plural* **fives.** one more than four; 5. *The child can count to five.*

fix /fiks/ *verb* **fixed, fix ing. 1.** to repair; mend. *I fixed the broken chair.* **2.** to get ready or arrange. *I will fix dinner.* —*noun, plural* **fix es. 3.** trouble; difficulty. *I got myself into quite a fix by promising to go to two parties on the same evening.*

flash /flash/ *verb* **flashed, flash ing. 1.** to burst out in sudden light or fire. **2.** to come or move quickly. *The headlights of the car were flashing.* —*noun, plural* **flash es.** a sudden, short burst of light or flame. *A flash of lightning lit the sky for an instant.*

float /flōt/ *noun, plural* **floats. 1.** anything that rests on top of water. A raft anchored in the swimming area of a lake is a float. **2.** a low flat platform on wheels that carries an exhibit in a parade. *Our float won first prize in the parade.* —*verb* **float ed, float ing. 1.** to rest on top of water or other liquid. *In swimming class we learned how to float on our backs.* **2.** to move along slowly in the air or on water. *Far above us, a balloon floated.*

flock /flok/ *noun, plural* **flocks.** a group of one kind. *The flock of sheep belongs to the farmer.*

/a/	at
/ā/	ape
/ä/	far
/â/	care
/e/	end
/ē/	me
/i/	it
/ī/	ice
/î/	pierce
/o/	hot
/ō/	old
/ô/	song
/ôr/	fork
/oi/	oil
/ou/	out
/u/	up
/ū/	use
/ü/	rule
/ů/	pull
/ûr/	turn
/ch/	chin
/ng/	sing
/sh/	shop
/th/	thin
/th/	this
/hw/	white
/zh/	treasure
/ə/	about
	taken
	pencil
	lemon
	circus

flop /flop/ *verb* **flopped, flop ping. 1.** to drop or fall heavily. *I was so tired, I couldn't wait to get home and flop into bed.* **2.** to fail completely. *The new restaurant flopped after being open only one month.*

fly[1] /flī/ *noun, plural* **flies.** one of a large group of insects that have two wings. *House flies, mosquitoes, and gnats are flies.*

fly[2] /flī/ *verb* **flew, flown, fly ing. 1.** to move through the air with wings. *Some birds fly south for the winter.* **2.** to pilot or travel in an aircraft. *The children flew to Puerto Rico to visit their grandparents.* **3.** to move, float. *I went to the park to fly my kite.*

fog /fôg, fog/ *noun, plural* **fogs.** a cloud of small drops of water close to the earth's surface. *The thick fog made driving dangerous.*

food /füd/ *noun, plural* **foods.** something that is eaten or taken in by people, animals, or plants that keeps them alive and helps them grow. *People need food to live.*

foot /fut/ *noun, plural* **feet. 1.** the end part of the leg that humans and other animals walk or stand on. *We have two feet.* **2.** a measure of length equal to 12 inches. One foot is the same as 0.3048 meters.

for /fôr/ *preposition* **1.** throughout a time or distance of. *We worked for two hours.* **2.** intended or reserved to keep. *This closet is for dishes.*

found /found/ *verb* past tense of *find*. See **find.**

four /fôr/ *noun, plural* **fours.** one more than three; 4. *The four animals were in a pen.*

free /frē/ *adjective* having one's liberty; not under other's control. *We kept the injured bird until its wing healed, and then we set him free.*

friend /frend/ *noun, plural* **friends.** a person whom one knows well and likes. *I like to play with my friends after school.*

frisk y /fris′ kē/ *adjective* **frisk i er, frisk i est.** playful; lively. *The puppy was frisky.*

frog /frôg, frog/ *noun, plural* **frogs.** a small animal with moist skin, webbed feet, and no tail. *Frogs are closely related to toads.*

front /frunt/ *noun, plural* **fronts. 1.** the part that faces forward or comes first. *This jacket has a zipper in the front.* **2.** a place or position ahead of the forward part. *He entered the store while I waited in front.*

full /fùl/ *adjective* **full er, full est. 1.** holding as much or as many as possible. *I poured myself a full glass of milk.* **2.** having or containing a large number or quantity. *We had a house full of guests for the party.*

gas /gas/ *noun* gasoline. *We filled the car's tank with gas.*

get /get/ *verb* **got, got ten, get ting.** to come to have or own; receive; gain; earn. *I hope to get a radio for my birthday. I got a good grade on the test.*

girl /gûrl/ *noun, plural* **girls.** a female child from birth to the time she is a young woman. *There are ten girls in my class.*

give /giv/ *verb* **gave, giv en.** to hand, pass, present, or grant. *My parents gave me a dog.*

glad /glad/ *adjective* **glad der, glad dest.** happy and pleased. *Our mother was glad we came home.*

glass /glas/ *noun, plural* **glass es.** a container used for drinking. *Please fill the glass with water.*

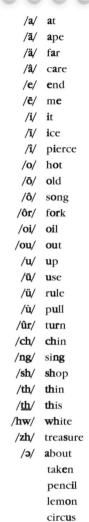

/a/ at
/ā/ ape
/ä/ far
/â/ care
/e/ end
/ē/ me
/i/ it
/ī/ ice
/î/ pierce
/o/ hot
/ō/ old
/ô/ song
/ôr/ fork
/oi/ oil
/ou/ out
/u/ up
/ū/ use
/ü/ rule
/ù/ pull
/ûr/ turn
/ch/ chin
/ng/ sing
/sh/ shop
/th/ thin
/<u>th</u>/ this
/hw/ white
/zh/ treasure
/ə/ about
　　 taken
　　 pencil
　　 lemon
　　 circus

globe /glōb/ *noun, plural* **globes. 1.** the world. *The group traveled around the globe and saw many interesting things.* **2.** a round ball with a map of the world on it. *We studied the oceans and continents on a globe in our classroom.*

glove /gluv/ *noun, plural* **gloves.** a covering for the hand. Most gloves have separate parts for each of the four fingers and for the thumb. However, boxing gloves and some baseball gloves hold four fingers together in one part. *I lost a glove.*

glue /glü/ *noun, plural* **glues.** a substance used for sticking things together. *Please use glue to put the vase back together.*

go /gō/ *verb* **went, gone, go ing.** to move or leave. *I go to school by bus.*

goat /gōt/ *noun, plural* **goats.** an animal that is related to the sheep. Goats have short horns and a tuft of hair under their chins that looks like a beard. They are raised in many parts of the world for their milk, hair, meat, and skin.

goes /gōz/ *verb* a form of the present of *go* that is used with he, she, it, or the name of a person, place, or thing. *That student goes to a piano lesson after school.*

gone /gôn/ *adjective* used up or spent. *The oranges are all gone.— verb* past participle of *go.* See **go.**

good /gůd/ *adjective* **bet ter, best. 1.** of high quality; not bad or poor. *The food at this restaurant is good.* **2.** nice or pleasant. *We had a good time.* **3.** behaving properly. *The children were good while you were gone.* **4.** real; true; genuine. *I have a good excuse for being late.*

goose /güs/ *noun, plural* **geese.** a bird that swims. Geese have webbed feet and are larger than ducks

got /got/ *verb* past tense of *get.* See **get.**

grade /grād/ *noun, plural* **grades.** a year or level of work at school. *Next year I will be in third grade.*

grand /grand/ *adjective* **grand er, grand est.** large and splendid. *The king and queen live in a grand palace.*

grand fa ther /grand′ fa′ th<u>ə</u>r/ *noun, plural* **grand fa thers.** the father of one's mother or father. *My grandfather will push the swing.*

grand moth er /grand′ mu<u>th</u>′ ər/ *noun, plural* **grand moth ers.** the mother of one's mother or father. *The song is one that my grandmother taught me.*

grape /grāp/ *noun, plural* **grapes.** a small juicy round fruit that grows on vines. *We like to eat grapes.*

grass /gras/ *noun, plural* **grass es.** any large number of plants that have narrow leaves. *The cow eats grass from the field.*

grin /grin/ *noun, plural* **grins.** a broad happy smile. *He had a grin on his face when he won.*

grow /grō/ *verb* **grew, grown, grow ing.** to become bigger. *That plant will grow quickly.*

grump /grump/ *noun* one you cannot please. *She is a grump until noon.—verb* **grumps, grumped, grump ing.** to talk of not being pleased. *Don't grump about the flat tire.*

• • • **H** • • • • • • • • • • • •

hand /hand/ *noun, plural* **hands.** the end of the arm from the wrist down. *There are four fingers and a thumb on a hand.*

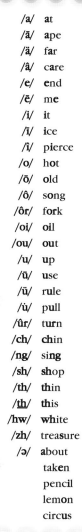

/a/	at
/ā/	ape
/ä/	far
/ā/	care
/e/	end
/ē/	me
/i/	it
/ī/	ice
/î/	pierce
/o/	hot
/ō/	old
/ô/	song
/ôr/	fork
/oi/	oil
/ou/	out
/u/	up
/ū/	use
/ü/	rule
/ù/	pull
/ûr/	turn
/ch/	chin
/ng/	sing
/sh/	shop
/th/	thin
/<u>th</u>/	this
/hw/	white
/zh/	treasure
/ə/	about
	taken
	pencil
	lemon
	circus

hard /härd/ *adverb* **1.** with effort or energy. *They worked hard on the farm.* **2.** with force or strength. *It rained so hard yesterday that the roads were flooded.*

harm /härm/ *noun, plural* **harms. 1.** injury or hurt. *To make sure no harm would come to the children, their parents made them wear life jackets when they went sailing.* **2.** an evil; wrong. *The child saw no harm in lying or stealing.*

has /haz/ *verb* a form of the present tense of *have* that is used with *he, she, it,* and the name of a person, place, or thing. *My friend has a new bicycle.*

hat /hat/ *noun, plural* **hats.** a covering for the head. It often has a brim and crown. *On cold days the baby wears a hat.*

hay /hā/ *noun, plural* **hays.** grass, alfalfa, or clover that is cut and dried to feed animals. *The farmer feeds hay to the cow.*

hid /hid/ *verb* past tense of *hide.* See **hide.**

hide /hīd/ *verb* **hid, hid den** or **hid, hid ing. 1.** to put or keep out of sight. **2.** to keep secret. *The lost children tried to hide their fears.*

his /hiz/ *pronoun* the one or ones that belong to or have to do with him. *This book is mine and that book is his.* — *adjective* of, belonging to, or having to do with him. *His best friend lives next door.*

hit /hit/ *verb* **hit, hit ting. 1.** to give a blow to; strike. *The bully hit my friend with a stick.* **2.** to send by striking with a bat or racket. *The batter hit the ball over the fence.*

hook /hùk/ *noun, plural* **hooks.** a bent piece of metal, wood, or other strong material that is used to hold something. *There is a row of coat hooks along the wall in the classroom.*—*verb* **hooked, hook ing.** to hang, fasten, or attach with a hook.

156

We hooked the wire hanger over the nail.

hop /hop/ *noun, plural* **hops.** a short jump or leap. *The bunny took three hops and was gone.* —*verb* **hopped, hop ping. 1.** to make a short jump on one foot. *When you play hopscotch, you have to hop on one foot.* **2.** to move by jumping on all feet at once. *Rabbits and frogs hop.*

horn /hôrn/ *noun, plural* **horns. 1.** a hard, pointed growth on the head of some animals that have hooves. Deer, sheep, and rhinoceroses have horns. **2.** a device used to make a loud warning sound. *The bus driver honked the horn at the children.*

horse /hôrs/ *noun, plural* **hors es.** a large animal with four legs, hooves, and a long flowing mane and tail. *Horses are used for riding and pulling heavy loads.*

house /hous/ *noun, plural* **hous es.** a building in which people live; home. *Our friends asked us to come to their house for dinner.*

howl /houl/ *verb* **howled, howl ing.** to make a loud, wailing cry. Dogs and wolves both howl. *The wind howls when it blows hard.*

hush /hush/ *noun* a silence or stillness that comes when a noise stops. *When the speaker raised his hand, there was a hush in the auditorium.*

if /if/ *conjunction* **1.** in case; in the event that; supposing that. *If I hurt your feelings, I'm sorry.* **2.** with the requirement or agreement that. *I can go to the movies if I finish my homework first.*

in side /in′ sīd′, in sīd′, in′ sīd′/ *noun, plural* **in sides.** the inner side or part; interior. *The inside of the house was dark.*

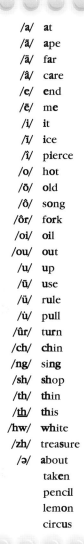

/a/ at
/ā/ ape
/ä/ far
/â/ care
/e/ end
/ē/ me
/i/ it
/ī/ ice
/î/ pierce
/o/ hot
/ō/ old
/ô/ song
/ôr/ fork
/oi/ oil
/ou/ out
/u/ up
/ū/ use
/ü/ rule
/u̇/ pull
/ûr/ turn
/ch/ chin
/ng/ sing
/sh/ shop
/th/ thin
/<u>th</u>/ this
/hw/ white
/zh/ treasure
/ə/ about
　　taken
　　pencil
　　lemon
　　circus

in to /in′ tü, in′ tə/ *preposition* **1.** to or toward the inside of. *We walked into the house.* **2.** to make contact with. *The child bumped into the door.*

jam [1] /jam/ *verb* **jammed, jam ming.** to press or squeeze into a tight space. *The traveler tried to jam too many clothes into one suitcase.* **2.** to become or cause to become stuck so as not to work. *The rifle jammed when the soldier tried to fire it.* —*noun, plural* **jams.** a difficult situation. *The driver was in a real jam when he locked his keys inside his car.*

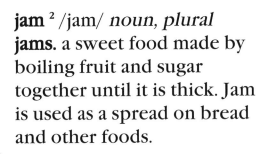

jam [2] /jam/ *noun, plural* **jams.** a sweet food made by boiling fruit and sugar together until it is thick. Jam is used as a spread on bread and other foods.

job /job/ *noun, plural* **jobs. 1.** a position of work; employment. *Did you get a job for the summer?* **2.** work that has to be done. *It's my job to feed and walk the dog.*

jog /jog/ *verb* **jogged, jog ging.** to run or move at a slow, steady pace. *My parents jog in the park every morning for exercise.*

jump /jump/ *verb* **jumped, jump ing.** to use a push from one's feet to move through or into the air. *He had to jump to catch the ball.*

just /just/ *adverb* by very little. *Because of the traffic you just missed the plane.*

kan ga roo /kang′ gə rü′/ *noun, plural* **kan ga roos** or **kan ga roo.** an animal that has small front legs, very strong back legs for leaping, and a long powerful tail for balance. The female kangaroo carries her young in a pouch for about six months after birth.

kick /kik/ *verb* **kicked,
kick ing.** to hit with the foot.
—*noun, plural* **kicks.** a hit or
blow with the foot. *The
child opened the door with
a kick.*

kind [1] /kīnd/ *adjective*
kind er, kind est. gentle,
generous, and friendly. *A
kind person is thoughtful of
others.*

kind [2] /kīnd/ *noun, plural*
kinds. a group of things that
are the same in some way.
*The whales are one kind of
mammal.*

kiss /kis/ *verb* **kissed,
kiss ing.** to touch with the
lips as a sign of greeting or
affection. *I kissed my aunt
and uncle before they left.* —
noun, plural **kiss es.** a touch
with the lips. *The child gave
her mother a kiss.*

· · · **L** · · · · · · · · · · · · · · · ·

land /land/ *verb* **land ed,
land ing.** to bring to the
ground. *The pilot will land
the plane.*

lap /lap/ *noun, plural* **laps.**
the front part of the body
between the waist and the
knees of a person who is
seated. *The girl sat on her
grandmother's lap.*

last /last/ *adjective* coming at
the end. *The baby is the last
to go to sleep.*

leave /lēv/ *verb* **left, leav ing.**
to omit. *We didn't have
enough onions for the stew,
so I left them out.*

light /līt/ *adjective* **light er,
light est. 1.** having little
weight; not heavy. *The
empty box was light.* **2.** not
great in force. *A light rain
fell.* **3.** moving easily;
graceful; nimble. *The
children were the lightest
on their feet.* —*noun, plural*
lights. the form of energy
that makes it possible for us
to see. *The sun gives off
light.*

li on /lī ən/ *noun, plural*
li ons. a large, strong
animal of the cat family.
*The lion lives mainly in
Africa and southern Asia.*

/a/	at
/ā/	ape
/ä/	far
/â/	care
/e/	end
/ē/	me
/i/	it
/ī/	ice
/î/	pierce
/o/	hot
/ō/	old
/ô/	song
/ôr/	fork
/oi/	oil
/ou/	out
/u/	up
/ū/	use
/ü/	rule
/ù/	pull
/ûr/	turn
/ch/	chin
/ng/	sing
/sh/	shop
/th/	thin
/th/	this
/hw/	white
/zh/	treasure
/ə/	about
	taken
	pencil
	lemon
	circus

159

The male has long, shaggy hair around its neck, head, and shoulders.

list /list/ *noun, plural* **lists.** a series of words, numbers, or other things. *The spelling words are in a list.*

live /liv/ *verb* **lived, liv ing.** to be alive; have life. *That ruler lived during the Middle Ages.*

lock /lok/ *noun, plural* **locks.** a fastener for a door, window, or a chest. *The front door has a lock.*

log /lôg, log/ *noun, plural* **logs. 1.** a piece of a tree cut with the bark still on. *The pioneer family used logs to build their cabin.* **2.** the record of the voyage of a ship or the flight of an airplane. *The captain of the ship kept a log.*

long /lông/ *adjective* **long er, long est.** great length; not short. *It's a long way from our school to the lake.*

look /lùk/ *noun, plural* **looks. 1.** the act of looking; a glance or inspection. *Take a look at this new bicycle.* **2.** appearance. *The guest had a cheerful look.* —*verb* **looked, look ing.** to use one's eyes; see. **1.** *I looked at my friend's stamp collection.* **2.** to turn one's eyes or attention. *Look at the camera and smile.*

lose /lüz/ *verb* **lost, los ing. 1.** to have no longer. *I lost my pencil.* **2.** to fail to win. *The team lost the game.*

lost /lôst/ *verb* past tense of *lose.* See **lose.**

lot /lot/ *noun, plural* **lots. 1.** a great amount. *There are a lot of cars on this road.* **2.** a piece of land. *We play baseball on an empty lot.*

loud /loud/ *adjective* **loud er, loud est. 1.** having a strong sound; not quiet. *The jet plane made a loud noise.* **2.** too bright; gaudy. *That is the loudest tie I've ever seen.* —*adverb* in a loud way. *We hear you loud and clear.*

luck /luk/ *noun* good fortune seeming to happen by chance. *Wish me luck!*

lunch /lunch/ *noun, plural* **lunch es.** a meal between breakfast and dinner. *They eat lunch at school.*

lunch room /lunch′ rüm′, lunch′ rùm′ / *noun* a place where light meals are served, especially a cafeteria in a school.

· · · **M** · · · · · · · · · ·

mad /mad/ *adjective* feeling or showing anger; angry. *I was mad when I found that my new bicycle was scratched.*

man /man/ *noun, plural* **men.** an adult male person. *The boy grew up to be a handsome man.*

man y /men′ ē/ *adjective* made up of a large number. *There are many books on American history.* —*noun* a large number. *The meeting*

of the club was canceled because many of the members could not be there. —*pronoun* a large number of people or things. *Many were late for school.*

map /map/ *noun, plural* **maps.** a drawing that shows the surface features of an area. Maps of large areas usually show cities, rivers, oceans, and other features. *He studied the map before he started the car's engine.*

march /märch/ *verb* **marched, march ing. 1.** to walk with regular, measured steps as soldiers do. People who march walk in step with others in an orderly group. **2.** to move forward steadily. *Time marches on.*

mask /mask/ *noun, plural* **masks.** a covering worn to hide or protect the face. *We wear masks at Halloween.*

may be /mā′ bē/ *adverb* possibly; perhaps. *I don't agree with you, but maybe you are right.*

/a/	at
/ā/	ape
/ä/	far
/â/	care
/e/	end
/ē/	me
/i/	it
/ī/	ice
/î/	pierce
/o/	hot
/ō/	old
/ô/	song
/ôr/	fork
/oi/	oil
/ou/	out
/u/	up
/ū/	use
/ü/	rule
/ù/	pull
/ûr/	turn
/ch/	chin
/ng/	sing
/sh/	shop
/th/	thin
/th/	this
/hw/	white
/zh/	treasure
/ə/	about
	taken
	pencil
	lemon
	circus

meal /mēl/ *noun, plural* **meals.** the food served or eaten at one time. *Breakfast is the first meal of the day.*

mean /mēn/ *verb* **meant, mean ing. 1.** to have in mind; want to do or say. *I do not know what you mean by that remark.* **2.** to have a purpose; intent. *I didn't mean to bake the cake so long.*

meat /mēt/ *noun, plural* **meats.** the parts of an animal used for food. The flesh of a cow, pig, or lamb is meat.

meet /mēt/ *noun, plural* **meets.** a meeting or contest. *Our school won first in the swimming meet.* —*verb* **met, meet ing.** to come to a place where one is facing someone or something coming from another direction. *While walking downtown, they met a friend they hadn't seen in months.*

mend /mend/ *verb* **mend ed, mend ing.** to put in good condition again. *Use glue to mend the dish.*

mess /mes/ *noun, plural* **mess es.** a disorderly condition; untidy. *Clean up the mess in your room.*

met /met/ *verb* the past tense and past participle of *meet. Have you met his friend?* See **meet.**

might /mīt/ *verb* an auxiliary verb that is used in the following ways: **1.** to express the past of *may. I asked my teacher if I might leave.* **2.** to say something is possible. *The story we heard might be true, but I'm not sure.* **3.** to ask permission. *Might I borrow your dictionary?* **4.** to offer a suggestion. *You might try using a pencil so that you can erase your mistakes.*

milk /milk/ *noun* a white liquid food produced by glands in female mammals. The milk of all mammals is used to feed their babies. The milk of cows is used as food by people.

mi nus /mī′ nəs/ *preposition*
1. decreased by; less. *Ten minus seven is three.* **2.** lacking; without. *The chair was minus a leg.*

mitt /mit/ *noun, plural* **mitts.** a type of glove used in baseball. Mitts have padding to protect a person's hand.

mix /miks/ *verb* **mixed, mix ing. 1.** to put two or more different things together. *We mixed yellow roses and white roses in the bouquet.* **2.** to blend, combine, or join. *Oil and water don't mix. —noun, plural* **mix es.** something that is made by mixing; mixture. *This cake was made from a packaged mix.*

moon /mün/ *noun, plural* **moons.** a heavenly body that revolves around the earth from west to east once every 29 1/2 days. The moon seems to shine because it reflects light from the sun.

moose /müs/ *noun, plural* **moose.** a large, heavy animal related to the deer that live in forests in cold northern regions of North America, Europe, and Asia. The male moose has enormous, broad antlers.

mop /mop/ *noun, plural* **mops.** a cleaning device made of a bundle of yarn or cloth or a sponge attached to a long handle. *Please use the mop to wipe up the water. — verb* **mopped, mop ping.** to clean or dry with a mop. *I mopped the floor.*

more /môr/ *adjective* greater in number. *A gallon is more than a quart. —adverb* to a greater amount. *Be more careful. —noun* an extra amount. *Our dogs always want more to eat.*

morn ing /môr ning/ *noun, plural* **morn ings.** the early part of the day. Morning ends at noon. *I slept late some mornings.*

moth er /muth′ ər/ *noun, plural* **moth ers.** a female parent. *My mother is pretty, and she is nice.*

/a/	at
/ā/	ape
/ä/	far
/â/	care
/e/	end
/ē/	me
/i/	it
/ī/	ice
/î/	pierce
/o/	hot
/ō/	old
/ô/	song
/ôr/	fork
/oi/	oil
/ou/	out
/u/	up
/ū/	use
/ü/	rule
/ů/	pull
/ûr/	turn
/ch/	chin
/ng/	sing
/sh/	shop
/th/	thin
/th/	this
/hw/	white
/zh/	treasure
/ə/	about
	taken
	pencil
	lemon
	circus

163

much /much/ *adjective* great in amount or degree. *I don't have much money left after buying that gift.*

mud /mud/ *noun* soft, wet dirt. *She had mud on her shoes.*

must /must/ *verb* an auxiliary verb that is used to express the following meanings: **1.** to be obliged to. *I must return this book.* **2.** to be forced. *People must eat to live.* **3.** to be likely to. *They must have forgotten.*

my self /mī self'/ *pronoun* **1.** my own self. *I cut myself.* **2.** my usual, normal, or true self. *I haven't been myself since the accident.*

night /nīt/ *noun, plural* **nights.** the time when it is dark; time between the setting and rising of the sun. *The baby slept seven nights without crying.*

nine /nīn/ *noun, plural* **nines.** one more than eight; 9. *There are nine boys on the team.*

no bod y /nō' bod' ē/ *noun, plural* **no bod ies.** a person of no importance or rank. *Be careful or you will be nobody.* —*pronoun* no person; no one. *I rang the doorbell, but nobody answered.*

nose /nōz/ *noun, plural* **nos es.** the part of the face or head that is used for breathing and smelling. Air comes into and goes out of the nose through the nostrils.

note book /nōt' bùk'/ *noun, plural* **note books.** a book with blank pages for notes. *Children take notebooks to school.*

now /nou/ *adverb* **1.** at this time; at this moment. *My friends are at the beach now, while I'm here working.* **2.** without delay. *Eat your food now.*

num ber /num′ bər/ *noun,* *plural* **num bers. 1.** the total amount of things in a group. *The number of children in the family is three.*
2. a symbol or word that tells how many. 2, 5, 77, and 396 are numbers.

off /ôf/ *preposition* no longer on, attached to, or connected with; away from. *A button is off my jacket.* —*adverb* so as to be no longer on, attached, or connected. *I broke a piece of bread off from the loaf.*

one /wun/ *noun, plural* **ones.** the first and lowest number; 1. *There is only one left.*

our /our/ *adjective* of, belonging to, or having to do with us. *Our house is on Oak Street.*

out /out/ *adverb* away from the center or from inside. *I turned on the faucet, and water gushed out.*

owl /oul/ *noun, plural* **owls.** a bird that has a round head with large, staring eyes and a hooked bill, a short square tail, and soft feathers. Owls eat mice, frogs, snakes, and insects and usually hunt at night.

pack /pak/ *verb* **packed, pack ing.** to press together. *Go pack your case.* —*noun, plural* **packs.** a group of things. *I see a large pack of wolves in the field.*

pail /pāl/ *noun, plural* **pails.** a round open container with a flat bottom and a curved handle. *The children carry sand and water in the pails.*

pain /pān/ *noun, plural* **pains.** a feeling of being hurt. *The blister gave me pain.*

par ent /pâr′ ənt/ *noun, plural* **par ents. 1.** a father or mother. *The lady and man are my parents.* **2.** a living thing, as an animal or plant,

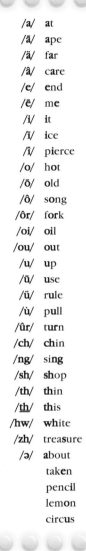

/a/ at
/ā/ ape
/ä/ far
/â/ care
/e/ end
/ē/ me
/i/ it
/ī/ ice
/î/ pierce
/o/ hot
/ō/ old
/ô/ song
/ôr/ fork
/oi/ oil
/ou/ out
/u/ up
/ū/ use
/ü/ rule
/ù/ pull
/ûr/ turn
/ch/ chin
/ng/ sing
/sh/ shop
/th/ thin
/<u>th</u>/ this
/hw/ white
/zh/ treasure
/ə/ about
      taken
      pencil
      lemon
      circus

that has produced offspring. *That animal is the parent of the little pup.*

park /pärk/ *noun, plural* **parks.** a piece of land, often having benches, trees, paths, and playgrounds, used by people for enjoyment and recreation. *We play ball in the park near our home.*

past /past/ *adjective* time gone by. *Vacation is past.*

pat /pat/ *verb* **pat ted, pat ting.** to tap or stroke gently with the hand. *I pat my dog when she obeys.*

path /path/ *noun, plural* **paths.** a trail or way for walking. *We had to shovel a path through the snow to our garages.*

pen /pen/ *noun, plural* **pens.** a tool for writing or drawing with ink. *Do the writing with pen and ink.*

per son /pûr′ sən/ *noun, plural* **per sons.** a man, woman, or child; human being. Every ten years, the government takes an official count of every person living in this country.

pin /pin/ *noun, plural* **pins.**
1. a short piece of wire with a pointed end, used for holding things together.
2. an ornament or badge that has a clasp for attaching it to clothing. *I wore a pin in the shape of a heart on my collar.* —*verb* **pinned, pin ning.** to hold together with a pin or pins. *My dress was too long, so I pinned the hem up.*

pine /pīn/ *noun, plural* **pines.** an evergreen tree that has cones and leaves that look like needles. *The wood from a pine is used in building and in making turpentine.*

plan /plan/ *noun, plural* **plans.** a way of doing something that has been thought out ahead of time. *Our plan for climbing the mountain is to zigzag up the south slope.*

planet /plan′ it/ *noun, plural* **planets.** one of nine large heavenly bodies that orbit the sun. The planets in our solar system are Mercury, Venus, Earth, Mars, Jupiter, Saturn, Uranus, Neptune, and Pluto.

plate /plāt/ *noun, plural* **plates.** a flat or shallow dish. *Food is served or eaten from plates.*

plot /plot/ *noun, plural* **plots.** 1. a secret plan. *The outlaws formed a plot to rob the stagecoach.* 2. the main story in a book, play, or movie. *That movie has an exciting plot.* 3. a small piece of ground. *We had our picnic on a grassy plot in the shade.*

plum /plum/ *noun, plural* **plums.** a soft, juicy fruit with a pit. *The tree has red plums.*

plus /plus/ *preposition* with the addition of. *Two plus two is four.*

pond /pond/ *noun, plural* **ponds.** a body of a small amount of water surrounded by land. *There are fish in the pond.*

pool /pül/ *noun, plural* **pools.** a tank of water to swim in, either indoors or outdoors. *The people next door to us have a pool.*

pull /pùl/ *verb* **pulled, pull ing.** to grab or hold something and move it forward or toward oneself. *Two horses pulled the wagon.*

push /pùsh/ *verb* **pushed, push ing.** 1. to press on something in order to move it. *I pushed the cart through the market.* 2. to move forward with effort. *We had to push through the crowd.*

put /pùt/ *verb* **put, put ting.** 1. to cause a thing or a person to be in a certain place, condition, or position; place; set. *Put the box on the table.* 2. to cause to undergo or experience. *You put them to a lot of trouble by being late.*

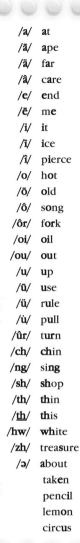

/a/	at
/ā/	ape
/ä/	far
/â/	care
/e/	end
/ē/	me
/i/	it
/ī/	ice
/î/	pierce
/o/	hot
/ō/	old
/ô/	song
/ôr/	fork
/oi/	oil
/ou/	out
/u/	up
/ū/	use
/ü/	rule
/ù/	pull
/ûr/	turn
/ch/	chin
/ng/	sing
/sh/	shop
/th/	thin
/th/	this
/hw/	white
/zh/	treasure
/ə/	about
	taken
	pencil
	lemon
	circus

rab bit /rab′ it/ *noun, plural* **rab bits.** a small animal that has long ears, a short tail, and soft fur. Rabbits live in burrows that they dig in the ground.

raise /rāz/ *verb* **raised, rais ing. 1.** to move or cause to move to a higher position. *I raised the flag.* **2.** to stir up or bring about. *Someone raised a commotion. —noun, plural* **rais es.** an increase in amount. *The worker received a raise in pay.*

rake /rāk/ *noun, plural* **rakes.** a tool that has a long handle with teeth or prongs attached at one end. It is used to gather leaves or smooth earth. *Use the rake on the cut grass.*

reach /rēch/ *verb* **reached, reach ing. 1.** to arrive at; come to. *We reached the cabin after walking two miles.* **2.** to touch or grasp.

I can't reach the top shelf of the bookcase.

read /rēd/ *verb* **read** /red/, **read ing. 1.** to look at and understand the meaning of something that is written. *I learned to read when I was in first grade.* **2.** the act of saying aloud something that is written. *The writer gave a reading of a new poem.*

rest /rest/ *noun* a time to relax. *She took a rest after working.*

rich /rich/ *adjective* **rich er, rich est. 1.** having much money, land, or other valuable things. **2.** having a lot of something. *Our country is rich in natural resources.*

ride /rīd/ *noun, plural* **rides. 1.** a short trip on an animal or vehicle. *We took a ride around the block on our bicycles.* **2.** a device on which people ride for amusement. *We tried all the rides at the fair. —verb* **rode, rid den, rid ing. 1.** to sit on a vehicle or animal and make it move in order to be carried on it. *He rides his bicycle to school.* **2.** to travel on or in a car, train, or other vehicle. *We rode through the town on the bus.* **3.** to be carried along. *The sailboat rode smoothly over the waves.*

right /rīt/ *adjective*
1. correct or true; free of mistakes. *The student gave the right answer.* **2.** just, moral, or good. *Telling the truth was the right thing to do.*

rip /rip/ *verb* **ripped, rip ping.** to tear or pull apart. *I ripped my pants on the fence.* —*noun, plural* **rips.** a torn place; tear. *You have a rip in your shirt.*

road /rōd/ *noun, plural* **roads.** a strip of pavement or cleared ground that people or vehicles use to go from one place to another. *The workers covered all the roads with rock.*

robin /rob′ in/ *noun, plural* **robins.** a bird that lives in North America and Europe. The robin that lives in America has a reddish orange breast and a black head and tail.

rock /rok/ *noun, plural* **rocks.** a piece of stone. *She picked up a rock.*

rode /rōd/ *verb* past tense of *ride.* See **ride.**

room /rüm, rùm/ *noun, plural* **rooms.** **1.** an area that is or may be taken up by something. *There was no room to park the car in the lot.* **2.** an area in a house or building that is separated or set off by walls. *Our house has seven rooms.*

row /rō/ *verb* **rowed, row ing.** to use oars to make a boat move. *We rowed the boat. We liked rowing the big boat.* —*noun, plural* **rows.** a series of people or things in a line. *A row of trees was planted in front of the house.*

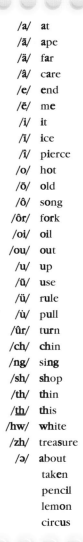

/a/	at
/ā/	ape
/ä/	far
/â/	care
/e/	end
/ē/	me
/i/	it
/ī/	ice
/î/	pierce
/o/	hot
/ō/	old
/ô/	song
/ôr/	fork
/oi/	oil
/ou/	out
/u/	up
/ū/	use
/ü/	rule
/ù/	pull
/ûr/	turn
/ch/	chin
/ng/	sing
/sh/	shop
/th/	thin
/th/	this
/hw/	white
/zh/	treasure
/ə/	about
	taken
	pencil
	lemon
	circus

rub /rub/ *verb* **rubbed, rub bing.** to press something back and forth with pressure. *Rub your hands with soap.*

rude /rüd/ *adjective* **rud er, rud est.** having or showing bad manners. *I've never met such a rude person.*

rug /rug/ *noun, plural* **rugs.** heavy fabric used to cover a floor. *There is a rug in front of the fireplace.*

run /run/ *verb* **ran, run, run ning. 1.** to go or cause to go quickly. *I ran for help when I saw the fire break out.* **2.** to read and follow the instructions in a program. *The computer is running that new program.*

rush /rush/ *verb* **rushed, rush ing. 1.** to move or go quickly. *We'll have to rush or we'll be late.* **2.** to act or do in a hurry. *Don't rush your work or you will make a mistake.*

rust /rust/ *noun, plural* **rusts.** a reddish brown or orange coating that forms on iron when it is exposed to moisture or air. *The gate will soon rust.*

sack /sak/ *noun, plural* **sacks.** a bag made of strong material. *Place the sack of potatoes on the floor.*

sail boat /sāl′ bōt′/ *noun, plural* **sail boats.** a boat that is moved by the wind blowing against its sail or sails. *We went on the lake in a sailboat.*

sand /sand/ *noun* loose grains of tiny crushed rock. *The beach is covered with sand.*

sand box /sand′ boks′/ *noun, plural* **sand box es.** a large, low box or enclosed area filled with sand for children to play in. *The men filled two sandboxes with clean sand for the children.*

say /sā/ *verb* **said, say ing.**
1. to speak or pronounce words. *What did you say?*
2. to repeat. *The class said the pledge.*

sea /sē/ *noun, plural* **seas.** the large body of salt water that covers almost three fourths of the earth's surface; ocean. *The crew struggled to keep the ship afloat in the rough seas.*

seal /sēl/ *noun, plural* **seals** or **seal.** a sea animal that lives in coastal waters and has flippers instead of feet. Seals spend some of their time on land.

seam /sēm/ *noun, plural* **seams.** a line formed by sewing together the edges of two or more pieces of cloth, leather, or other material. *One of the seams in this coat is coming apart.*

sec ond [1] /sekʹ ənd/ *adjective* next after the first. *I liked the movie better the second time I saw it.* —*noun, plural* **sec onds.** a person or thing that is next in line after the first. *She was second in line.* —*verb* **sec ond ed.** to help or support. *Who will second the motion to end the meeting?*

sec ond [2] /sekʹ ənd/ *noun, plural* **sec onds.** one of the sixty equal parts of a minute.

see /sē/ *verb* **saw, seen, see ing. 1.** to look or look at with the eyes. *I see better with glasses.* **2.** to understand. *I see what you mean.* **3.** to experience. *Those old shoes have seen much wear.*

seem /sēm/ *verb* **seemed, seem ing. 1.** to appear to be. *The dark clouds make it seem later than it is.* **2.** to appear to oneself. *I seem to have forgotten your name.*

seen /sēn/ *verb* past participle of *see.* See **see.**

send /send/ *verb* **sent, send ing.** to cause to go, come, or be. *Send the card to the lady next door.*

/a/	at
/ā/	ape
/ä/	far
/â/	care
/e/	end
/ē/	me
/i/	it
/ī/	ice
/î/	pierce
/o/	hot
/ō/	old
/ô/	song
/ôr/	fork
/oi/	oil
/ou/	out
/u/	up
/ū/	use
/ü/	rule
/ù/	pull
/ûr/	turn
/ch/	chin
/ng/	sing
/sh/	shop
/th/	thin
/th/	this
/hw/	white
/zh/	treasure
/ə/	about
	taken
	pencil
	lemon
	circus

sev en /sev′ ən/ *noun, plural.* **sev ens.** one more than six; 7. *There are seven boys on the porch.*

shack /shak/ *noun, plural* **shacks.** a small, roughly built cabin. *We play in the shack.*

shad ow /shad′ ō/ *noun, plural* **shad ows. 1.** a dark area or figure made when rays of light are blocked by a person or thing. *The child cast a shadow.* **2.** a slight amount; suggestion. *There is not a shadow of a doubt that they are lying.*

shake /shāk/ *verb* **shook, sha ken, sha king.** to move quickly up and down, back and forth, or from side to side.

shall /shal/ *verb* an auxiliary verb that is used in the following ways: **1.** to express future actions and conditions. *I shall be happy to see you.* **2.** to express a requirement. *You shall do as I say.* **3.** to ask a question that extends an invitation or

offers a suggestion. *Shall we dance?*

shame /shām/ *noun* **1.** a painful feeling caused by having done something wrong or foolish. *He felt shame for having cheated.* **2.** a thing to be sorry for. *It was a shame that our team lost.*

share /shâr/ *verb* **shared, shar ing.** to use with another or others. *Two of us shared a tent.* **2.** to divide into portions and give to others as well as to oneself. *I shared my sandwich.*

sharp /shärp/ *adjective* **sharp er.** having an edge or point that cuts or pierces easily. *That knife has a sharp blade.*

sheep /shēp/ *noun, plural* **sheep.** an animal with a thick, heavy coat that is raised on farms for its wool and meat. *They made the wool of the sheep into yarn.*

shine /shīn/ *verb* **shone** or **shined, shin ing.** to give or reflect light. *The stars shine at night.*

shirt /shûrt/ *noun, plural* **shirts.** a piece of clothing worn on the upper part of the body. One kind of shirt has a collar, sleeves, and buttons down the front.

shock /shok/ *noun, plural* **shocks.** a sudden, violent upsetting of the mind or emotions. *The parents never got over the shock of their child's accident.*

shook /shùk/ *verb* past tense of *shake.* See **shake.**

shoot /shüt/ *noun, plural* **shoots.** a new or young plant or stem. *The plant started from a small shoot.* —*verb* **shot, shoot ing. 1.** to hit with a bullet, arrow, or the like. *Hunters shoot deer with rifles.* **2.** to send forth from a weapon. *I shot an arrow at the target.* **3.** to come forth. *The bean plants are shooting up from the ground.*

shore /shôr/ *noun, plural* **shores. 1.** the land along the edge of an ocean, lake, or large river. *We walked along the shore.* **2.** land. *The sailors were glad to be back on shore after the long voyage.*

short /shôrt/ *adjective* not long or tall. *The grass is short.* —*adverb* in a sudden or unexpected way. *The horse stopped short, and the rider fell off.*

shut /shut/ *verb* **shut, shut ting. 1.** to block or cover an entrance; close. *We shut the window.* **2.** to become closed. *The door shut behind me.*

shy /shī/ *adjective* **1.** not comfortable around other people. *The shy child wouldn't come into the room.* **2.** easily frightened. *Animals that live in the woods are usually too shy to get close to people.*

sick /sik/ *adjective* **sick er, sick est.** poor health. *My friend is sick with a cold.*

/a/	at
/ā/	ape
/ä/	far
/â/	care
/e/	end
/ē/	me
/i/	it
/ī/	ice
/î/	pierce
/o/	hot
/ō/	old
/ô/	song
/ôr/	fork
/oi/	oil
/ou/	out
/u/	up
/ū/	use
/ü/	rule
/ù/	pull
/ûr/	turn
/ch/	chin
/ng/	sing
/sh/	shop
/th/	thin
/th/	this
/hw/	white
/zh/	treasure
/ə/	about
	taken
	pencil
	lemon
	circus

173

sight /sīt/ *verb* **sight ed, sight ing.** to see with the eyes. *The group finally sighted the cabin.* —*noun, plural* **sights. 1.** the power to see. *My glasses helped improve my sight.* **2.** the act of seeing. *I recognized you at first sight.*

sis ter /sis′ tər/ *noun, plural* **sis ters. 1.** a girl or woman with the same mother and father as another person. *I have two sisters.* **2.** a woman who belongs to a religious order. A nun is the same as sister in a religious order.

six /siks/ *noun, plural* **six es.** one more than five; 6. *We counted off the teams in sixes.*

skip /skip/ *verb* **skipped, skip ping. 1.** to spring or bound along, hopping lightly on one foot and then on the other. *The children skipped down the path.* **2.** to jump or leap over. *We skipped rope in the playground.* **3.** to pass or leave out. *Skip the*

arithmetic problems you can't do.

slam /slam/ *noun, plural* **slams.** a forceful and noisy closing or striking. *The door closed with a slam.* —*verb* **slammed, slam ming.** to close with force and a loud noise. *Please don't slam the door.*

slant /slant/ *noun, plural* **slants.** a sloping direction, line, or surface. *Hang the picture straight, not on a slant.* —*verb* **slant ed, slant ing.** to run or slope away from a straight line. *The roof slants toward the ground.*

sled /sled/ *noun, plural* **sleds.** a wooden framework mounted on runners. *A sled is used to carry people or loads over the snow.*

sleep /slēp/ *noun* **1.** a time or condition of rest that occurs naturally and regularly in humans and other animals. *I sleep eight hours a night.* **2.** a condition that resembles sleep. A hibernating bear is sometimes said to be sleeping. *The bear sleeps almost all winter.*

slick /slik/ *adjective* **slick er, slick est. 1.** smooth and shiny. *The horse had a slick coat.* **2.** smooth and slippery. *A newly waxed floor is slick.* —*noun, plural* **slicks.** a smooth or slippery place on a surface. *The boat left a slick of oil on the water.*

slide /slīd/ *noun, plural* **slides. 1.** the act of sliding. *Let's slide down the hill in our sleds.* **2.** a smooth surface for sliding. *I like to use the slide at school.* —*verb* **slid or slid ing. 1.** to move or cause to move smoothly, easily, quietly. *My friend slid into the seat next to me.* **2.** to fall or move suddenly from a position. *The truck slid off the icy road into a ditch.*

slip [1] /slip/ *noun, plural* **slips.** a small piece of paper, cloth, or any other material. *I wrote my friend's telephone number on a slip of paper.*

slip [2] /slip/ *verb* **slipped, slip ping.** to move suddenly from a position or out of control. *The man slipped on the ice.*

slot /slot/ *noun, plural* **slots.** a narrow, straight opening or groove. *Put the coin in the slot.*

slow /slō/ *adjective* **slow er, slow est. 1.** acting, moving, or happening with little speed. *The student was slow to answer the question.* **2.** behind the correct time. *Your watch is slow.*

sly /slī/ *adjective* **sli er, sli est. 1.** clever and shrewd; crafty. *The sly thief was never caught.* **2.** mischievous in a playful way. *The fox is slier than the chicken. He is the sliest of all.*

smart /smärt/ *adjective* **smart er, smart est.** clever or intelligent; bright. *She is a smart girl who does well in school.*

175

snack /snak/ *noun, plural* **snacks.** a small amount of food or drink eaten between regular meals. *I had a snack after school.*

snake /snāk/ *noun, plural* **snakes.** a kind of animal that has a long body covered with scales and no legs, arms, or wings. Snakes are reptiles that move by curving and then straightening out their bodies.

sneeze /snēz/ *verb* **sneezed, sneez ing.** to put forth air from the nose and mouth in a sudden, violent way. *When I have a cold I sneeze.*

snow /snō/ *noun, plural* **snows.** soft, white crystals of ice that fall to earth as precipitation. Snow is formed when water vapor freezes in the air.

soap /sōp/ *noun, plural* **soaps.** a substance used for washing and cleaning. Soap is usually made with fats and lye. Soaps are made in the form of bars, powders, and liquids.

soggy /sog′ ē/ *adjective* **sog gi er, sog gi est.** very wet or damp; soaked. *The ground was soggy after the heavy rain.*

some thing /sum′ thing′/ *adverb* to some extent; somewhat. *Your house looks something like ours.* — *pronoun* a thing that is not known or stated. *Something is wrong with our car.*

song /sông/ *noun, plural* **songs.** music with words or other vocal sounds. *The words of the song are pretty.*

soon /sün/ *adverb* **1.** in a short time. *Come to visit us again soon.* **2.** before the expected time. *The guests arrived too soon, and we weren't ready.*

sound [1] /sound/ *noun, plural* **sounds.** what can be heard.

sound [2] /sound/ *verb* **sound ed, sound ing.** to

make or cause to make a noise that can be heard. *The bell sounded at nine o'clock.*

south /south/ *adjective* toward or in the south. *A south wind was blowing.* — *noun* south is a direction. *South is one of the four main points of the compass.*

space /spās/ *noun, plural* **spac es.** the area in which the whole universe exists. *The planet earth and everything and everyone on it exist in space.*

spark /spärk/ *noun, plural* **sparks.** a small bit of burning or glowing material. *Sparks fly off burning wood.*

speak /spēk/ *verb* **spoke, spo ken. 1.** to use or utter words; talk. *The baby cannot speak yet.* **2.** to make known or express an idea, fact, or feeling. *She always speaks the truth.*

speech /spēch/ *noun, plural* **speech es. 1.** the ability to use spoken words to express ideas, thoughts, and feelings.

Animals do not have the power of speech. **2.** something that is spoken; talk. *The president's speech was broadcast on television.* **3.** a way in which someone speaks. *Your speech shows no trace of an accent.*

speed /spēd/ *noun, plural* **speeds. 1.** Quick or fast motion. *She ran with great speed and won the race.* **2.** the rate of motion. *He drove the car at a speed of forty miles per hour.* —*verb* **sped** or **speed ed, speed ing.** to go or cause to go quickly or rapidly. *We sped down the hill on our sleds.*

spin /spin/ *verb* **spun, spin ning. 1.** to turn quickly. *The child spun the top.* **2.** to make thin fibers into thread. *They spun the fibers into thread.* **3.** to make a web or cocoon. *Spiders spin webs.*

spoke [1] /spōk/ *noun, plural* **spokes.** one of the rods or bars that connect the rim of a wheel to the hub. *The spoke was broken on the wheel of my bike.*

/a/	at
/ā/	ape
/ä/	far
/â/	care
/e/	end
/ē/	me
/i/	it
/ī/	ice
/î/	pierce
/o/	hot
/ō/	old
/ô/	song
/ôr/	fork
/oi/	oil
/ou/	out
/u/	up
/ū/	use
/ü/	rule
/ù/	pull
/ûr/	turn
/ch/	chin
/ng/	sing
/sh/	shop
/th/	thin
/th/	this
/hw/	white
/zh/	treasure
/ə/	about
	taken
	pencil
	lemon
	circus

spoke [2] /spōk/ *verb* past tense of *speak*. See **speak**.

spoon /spün/ *noun, plural* **spoons.** a utensil with a small, shallow bowl at one end of a handle. A spoon is used for eating, measuring, or stirring.

spot /spot/ *noun, plural* **spots. 1.** a place. *That park is a pleasant spot for a picnic.* **2.** a mark or stain left by dirt, food, or other matter. *There is a spot of ketchup on your collar.*

spy /spī/ *noun, plural* **spies.** a person who watches others secretly. *A person is sometimes hired as a spy by the government.* —*verb* **spied, spy ing.** to watch others secretly. *The submarine was sent to spy on enemy ships.*

stack /stak/ *noun, plural* **stacks.** pile of hay, grass, or straw. *The hay is in a big stack.*

stain /stān/ *noun, plural* **stains.** a mark or spot. *There is an ink stain on the carpet.*

stamp /stamp/ *noun, plural* **stamps.** a small piece of paper that is stuck on letters and packages for the mailing fee. *Put a stamp on my letter.*

stand /stand/ *verb* **stood, stand ing.** to be upright on one's feet. *Tom will stand and wait for the bus.*

start /stärt/ *verb* **start ed, start ing.** to begin to act, move, or happen. *What time does the game start?*

stem /stem/ *noun, plural* **stems.** the main part of a plant that supports the leaves and flowers. *The flower broke off its stem.*

stick [1] /stik/ *noun, plural* **sticks.** a thin, long piece of wood. *Put a stick of wood on the fire.*

stick [2] /stik/ *verb* **sticks, stuck, stick ing.** to put on or attach. *Stick the stamp on the letter.*

sting /sting/ *verb* **stung, sting ing.** a sharp pain or hurt. *A bee will sting you.*

stood /stùd/ *verb* past tense and past participle of *stand.* See **stand.**

store /stôr/ *noun, plural* **stores. 1.** a place where goods are sold. *They went to the grocery store.* **2.** a supply of things put away for future use. *A store of firewood is in the garage.*

stripe /strīp/ *noun, plural* **stripes.** a long, narrow band. *Your shirt has red and white stripes.*

stuck /stuk/ *verb* past tense of *stick.* See **stick.**

such /such/ *adjective* of the same kind; of that kind. *I have never seen such weather.*

take /tāk/ *verb,* **took, tak en, tak ing. 1.** to get a hold of; grasp. *The student took a book from the shelf.* **2.** to capture or win by using force or skill. *My friend's painting took first prize.* **3.** to obtain; get. *The nurse took my temperature.* **4.** to carry with one; bring. *My parents took two suitcases on their trip.*

tap /tap/ *verb* **tapped, tap ping.** to hit or strike lightly again and again. *I tapped out the beat to the music.*

task /task/ *noun, plural* **tasks.** work to be done. *The writing will be a small task.*

teach /tēch/ *verb* **taught, teach ing.** to help a person learn; show how. *My neighbor teaches swimming in a camp and taught me to swim last summer.*

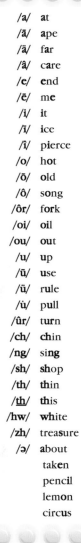

/a/	at
/ā/	ape
/ä/	far
/â/	care
/e/	end
/ē/	me
/i/	it
/ī/	ice
/î/	pierce
/o/	hot
/ō/	old
/ô/	song
/ôr/	fork
/oi/	oil
/ou/	out
/u/	up
/ū/	use
/ü/	rule
/ù/	pull
/ûr/	turn
/ch/	chin
/ng/	sing
/sh/	shop
/th/	thin
/th/	this
/hw/	white
/zh/	treasure
/ə/	about
	taken
	pencil
	lemon
	circus

team /tēm/ *noun, plural* **teams.** a group that plays, acts, or works together. *A team of scientists discovered a cure for the disease.*

ten /ten/ *noun, plural* **tens.** one more than nine; 10.

test /test/ *noun, plural* **tests.** a set of problems or tasks. *We have a spelling test on Friday.*

thank /thangk/ *verb* **thanked, thank ing. 1.** to say that one is grateful to. *I thanked the teacher for helping me.* **2.** to hold responsible. *I have you to thank for getting us into this mess.*

that /th̲at/ *adjective* used to indicate a person or thing being looked at or already mentioned. *Who wrote that book?*

them /th̲em/ *pronoun* the persons or things being talked about. *I ran to my grandparents and hugged them.*

thick /thik/ *adjective* **thick er, thick est. 1.** having much space between one side or surface and another. *The outside wall of the building is thick.* **2.** growing or being close; dense. *The fog was thickest near the river.*

thin /thin/ *adjective* **thin ner, thin nest.** having little space between one side or surface and the other; not thick. *The thin wrapping paper did not hide the title of the book.*

thing /thing/ *noun, plural* **things. 1.** whatever is spoken of, thought of, or done. *That was an unkind thing to say.* **2.** the general state of affairs. *How are things at school?*

think /thingk/ *verb* **thought, think ing. 1.** to use the mind to form ideas or to make decisions. *Think carefully before you answer.* **2.** to have or form in the mind as an opinion, belief, or idea. *The teacher thought we were related.* **3.** to call to mind or remember. *I was thinking of my grandmother.*

third /thûrd/ *adjective* next after the second. *They were third in the line. —noun, plural* **thirds.** one of three equal parts. *Cut the apple in thirds.*

those /<u>th</u>ōz/ *adjective* plural of *that.* See **that.**

three /thrē/ *noun, plural* **threes.** one more than two; 3. *The three of us will play the game.*

ti ger /tī gər/ *noun, plural* **ti gers.** a large animal that is a member of the cat family. Most tigers have an orange or yellow coat with black or brown stripes. Tigers live in Asia.

tight /tīt/ *adjective* 1. held firmly; secure. *Make a tight knot so the string won't come loose.* 2. made so that the parts are close together. *This sweater is very warm because it has such tight*

knit. 3. fitting the body closely. *My belt was tight after I ate that big dinner.*

tip /tip/ *noun, plural* **tips.** 1. the end part or point. *The tips of the fingers are very sensitive.* 2. a small piece that forms the end of something. *The cane had a shiny, rounded tip.*

to /tü; *unstressed* tù, tə/ *preposition* 1. in the direction of; toward. *Turn to the left.* 2. on, upon, or against. *Tack the carpet to the floor.*

toad /tōd/ *noun, plural* **toads.** an animal that looks something like a frog. A toad has rough dry skin and spends most of its time on land rather than water. Toads are amphibians.

toast /tōst/ *noun* sliced bread that has been browned by heat. —*verb* **toast ed, toast ing.** to brown by heating. *We ate many pieces of toast.*

/a/ at
/ā/ ape
/ä/ far
/â/ care
/e/ end
/ē/ me
/i/ it
/ī/ ice
/î/ pierce
/o/ hot
/ō/ old
/ô/ song
/ôr/ fork
/oi/ oil
/ou/ out
/u/ up
/ū/ use
/ü/ rule
/ù/ pull
/ûr/ turn
/ch/ chin
/ng/ sing
/sh/ shop
/th/ thin
/<u>th</u>/ this
/hw/ white
/zh/ treasure
/ə/ about
taken
pencil
lemon
circus

181

to geth er /tə geth′ ər/ *adverb* **1.** with one another. *The friends walked to school together.* **2.** into one gathering or mass. *Mix the butter and sugar together.* **3.** in agreement or cooperation. *Let's work together to solve this problem.* **4.** considered as a whole. *Alaska is larger than Texas, California, and Montana together.*

too /tü/ *adverb* **1.** in addition; also. *I love to read, but I like movies, too.* **2.** more than is needed or wanted. *I am too short.*

took /tùk/ *verb* past tense of *take.* See **take.**

tooth /tüth/ *noun, plural* **teeth.** one of the hard, white, bony parts of the mouth. Teeth are used for biting and chewing food and also in talking.

town /toun/ *noun, plural* **towns.** an area with buildings where people live and work. *A town is usually larger than a village but smaller than a city.*

trade /trād/ *noun, plural* **trades. 1.** the business of buying and selling goods. *The United States engages in much foreign trade.* **2.** the giving of one thing in return for something else. *The farmer makes trades of milk for eggs.*

trail /trāl/ *verb* **trails, trailed, trail ing.** to follow behind. *The children trailed the parade.* —*noun, plural* **trails.** a path through an area. *The people followed a marked trail.*

train /trān/ *noun, plural* **trains.** a line of railroad cars connected together. *Some trains carry passengers.* —*verb* **trained, train ing.** to teach to behave, think, or grow up in a certain way. *The parents trained their children to respect the rights of others.*

tramp /tramp/ *noun, plural* **tramps.** a person who

wanders from place to place and has no home. *The tramp asked for food.* —verb **tramped, tramp ing. 1.** to walk or step heavily. *Don't tramp on the flowers.* **2.** to travel on foot; walk or hike. *They spent the day tramping through the woods.*

tray /trā/ *noun, plural* **trays.** a flat, open container with a low rim to carry things or display things. *Waiters often carry food on trays.*

treat /trēt/ *noun, plural* **treats.** Something that is a special pleasure. *Going to the circus was a treat.* —verb **treat ed, treat ing.** to behave toward or deal with in a certain way. *The principal treated the student fairly.*

tree /trē/ *noun, plural* **trees.** a plant made up of a single main stem. *A tree has branches and leaves.*

trick /trik/ *noun, plural* **tricks. 1.** an action done to fool or cheat someone. **2.** a clever or skillful act. *The*

magician pulled a rabbit out of a hat and did many other tricks. —verb **tricked, trick ing.** to fool or cheat with a trick. *We tried to trick the teacher into letting us leave early.*

trim /trim/ *verb* **trimmed, trim ming.** to cut away parts to make things neat and orderly. *My dad will trim the hedge.*

trip /trip/ *verb* **tripped, trip ping.** to stumble or fall. *I tripped on the rug.* —noun, *plural* **trips.** the act of traveling.

truck /truk/ *noun, plural* **trucks.** a large motor vehicle to haul things. *There is rock on the truck.*

try /trī/ *verb* **tried, try ing.** to make an effort. *I will try to do my best.*

tube /tüb, tūb/ *noun, plural* **tubes.** a hollow piece of glass, rubber, plastic, or metal in the shape of a long pipe, used to carry liquids or

/a/	at
/ā/	ape
/ä/	far
/â/	care
/e/	end
/ē/	me
/i/	it
/ī/	ice
/î/	pierce
/o/	hot
/ō/	old
/ô/	song
/ôr/	fork
/oi/	oil
/ou/	out
/u/	up
/ū/	use
/ü/	rule
/ù/	pull
/ûr/	turn
/ch/	chin
/ng/	sing
/sh/	shop
/th/	thin
/th/	this
/hw/	white
/zh/	treasure
/ə/	about
	taken
	pencil
	lemon
	circus

gases. *A garden hose is a long tube.*

tug /tug/ *verb* **tugged, tug ging.** to give a pull on something. *The horses tugged the heavy wagon.* — *noun, plural* **tugs.** a hard pull. *Suddenly I felt a tug on the fishing line.*

tune /tün, tūn/ *noun, plural* **tunes. 1.** a series of musical tones that form a pleasing, easily remembered unit. *We hummed the tune when we couldn't remember the words.* **2.** a song. *The band played a few popular tunes.*

twin /twin/ *noun, plural* **twins.** one of two children or animals born at the same time to the same mother. *Some twins look exactly alike.*

two /tü/ *noun, plural* **twos.** one more than one; 2. *There were two birds on the wire.*

un cle /ung′ kəl/ *noun, plural* **un cles. 1.** the brother of one's mother or father. *My uncle will go with me.* **2.** the husband of one's aunt.

us /us/ *pronoun* the persons who are speaking or writing. *The neighbors invited us to dinner.*

ver y /ver′ ē/ *adjective* mere; by itself. *The very idea of having to get up early makes me groan.* — *adverb* to a high degree. *I am very sorry that you are not feeling well.*

week end /wēk′ end′/ *noun, plural* **week ends.** the period of time from Friday night or Saturday morning until Sunday night or Monday morning. *We went to the country for the weekend.*

went /went/ *verb* past tense of *go*. See **go**.

were /wûr/ *verb* a form of the past tense of *be* that is used with *you, we, they,* or the plural form of a noun. *We were at home all day.*

west /west/ *noun* the direction where the sun sets. *Look to the west to see the beautiful sunset.*

whale /hwāl, wāl/ *noun, plural* **whales.** a large animal that has a body like a fish. Whales are found in all oceans and in certain fresh waters. A whale is a mammal.

what /hwut, hwot, wut, wot/ *pronoun* **1.** used to ask questions about persons or things. *What is today's date?* **2.** the thing that. *They knew what I was thinking.*

wheel /hwēl, wēl/ *noun, plural* **wheels.** a round frame or solid object used on cars and wagons. *The car has four wheels.*

where /hwâr, wâr/ *adverb* in, at, to, or from what place. *Where did they go?*

while /hwīl/ *conjunction* during or in the time that. *Did anyone call while I was away?* —*noun* a period of time. *We stopped walking and rested for a while.*

whirl /hwûrl, wûrl/ *noun, plural* **whirls.** dizzy condition. *My head was in a whirl after I hit the ball.* —*verb* **whirled, whirl ing.** to turn or cause to turn quickly in a circle. *The blades of the fan are whirling.*

whisk er /hwis′ kər, wis′ kər/ *noun, plural* **whisk ers.** **1.** the hair growing on a man's face. *My dad has whiskers on his face before he shaves.* **2.** a stiff hair that grows on the face. *Cats and dogs have whiskers.*

/a/	at
/ā/	ape
/ä/	far
/â/	care
/e/	end
/ē/	me
/i/	it
/ī/	ice
/î/	pierce
/o/	hot
/ō/	old
/ô/	song
/ôr/	fork
/oi/	oil
/ou/	out
/u/	up
/ū/	use
/ü/	rule
/u̇/	pull
/ûr/	turn
/ch/	chin
/ng/	sing
/sh/	shop
/th/	thin
/th/	this
/hw/	white
/zh/	treasure
/ə/	about
	taken
	pencil
	lemon
	circus

whis per /hwis′ pər, wis′ pər/ *verb* to speak or say very softly. *My friend whispered a secret to me. —noun, plural* **whis pers.** *The teacher heard whispers from the back of the room.*

who /hü/ *pronoun* **1.** what or which person or persons. *Who gave you that pen?* **2.** that. *The student who wrote that story has a good sense of humor.*

why /hwī, wī/ *adverb* for what reason or purpose. *Why are you laughing?*

wide /wīd/ *adjective.* **1.** made up of or covering a large area from side to side. *There is a wide porch across the back of the house.* **2.** having a certain distance from side to side. *The room is 12 feet wide.* **3.** fully opened. *The child's eyes were wide with excitement.*

wind /wind/ *noun* air moving over the earth. *The wind blew the tree over.*

wing /wing/ *noun, plural* **wings.** movable parts of the body used for flying. *The bird has a broken wing.*

wish /wish/ *noun, plural* **wish es. 1.** a feeling of wanting something; a strong desire. **2.** a thing that a person wants. *I hoped for a compass for my birthday, and I got my wish. —verb* **wished, wish ing.** to want something very much; have a wish. *I wish that summer would last longer.*

with /with, with/ *preposition* **1.** in the company or keeping of. *We went to the movie with friends.* **2.** having or possessing. *We need someone with good skills for the job.*

wool /wul/ *noun, plural* **wools.** the soft, thick, curly hair of sheep and some other animals such as the llama and alpaca. Wool is spun into yarn which is made into cloth.

Y

yard /yärd/ *noun, plural* **yards.** an area of ground next to or surrounding a house, school, or other building. *We have a vegetable garden in our yard.*

yet /yet/ *adverb* at the present time. *I have never yet been late.*

your /yu̇r, yôr; *unstressed* yər/ *adjective* of or belonging to you. *Let's meet tomorrow at your house.*

Z

ze bra /zē′ brə/ *noun, plural* **ze bras** or **ze bra.** a wild animal that looks like a horse with a black-and-white striped coat. Zebras come from southern and eastern Africa.

zoo /zü/ *noun, plural* **zoos.** a park or public place where wild animals are kept for people to see. *The children went to the zoo to see the animals.*

/a/	at
/ā/	ape
/ä/	far
/â/	care
/e/	end
/ē/	me
/i/	it
/ī/	ice
/î/	pierce
/o/	hot
/ō/	old
/ô/	song
/ôr/	fork
/oi/	oil
/ou/	out
/u/	up
/ū/	use
/ü/	rule
/u̇/	pull
/ûr/	turn
/ch/	chin
/ng/	sing
/sh/	shop
/th/	thin
/th/	this
/hw/	white
/zh/	treasure
/ə/	about
	taken
	pencil
	lemon
	circus